Best Wishes
Don McGookey

Geologic Wonders
Of
South Park, Colorado

By

Donald P. McGookey

Published by Donald P. McGookey
203 West Wall Suite 705
Midland, Texas, 79701

First Edition, 2002

For Ordering Information Contact:

Donald P. McGookey
203 West Wall Suite 705
Midland Texas, 79701
(915) 686-0049
Email: dmcgookeys@juno.com

ISBN 0-9719271-0-3

Printed in Korea

This book is dedicated with love and appreciation to

Dr. Charles A. Waggoner

1927 - 2002

NASA Space Photo STS040-604-011. View is towards the northwest from high over Trinidad Colorado.
CC=Canon City, CS = Colorado Springs and F = Fairplay. Pikes Peak is the snow-covered mountain
northwest of Colorado Springs. Features in and around South Park that can be identified include the Upper
Arkansas Rift, Red Hill and Reinecker Ridge, the area of the Elkhorn Overthrust and with a close look, the
Guffey Caldera. Features across the top of the photo from left are Salt Lake, Uinta Mountains, Wind River
Mountains and the southeastern part of Big Horn Mountains. Obviously a very clear day. Image courtesy
of Earth Science and Image Analysis Laboratory, NASA Johnson Space Center. Web site:
eol.jsc.nasa.gov/sseop

Contents

Road Logs

Introduction

"We reached the head of the North Platte, on Kenosha Hill...We were well prepared, as we reached the top to be astonished at the sight of South Park, which from this point is a view of grandeur never to be forgotten. Prairies surrounded with high mountains and interspersed with pine-groves and small peaks---a very Eden Park---are a sight seldom surpassed even in the Rocky Mountains."

Fr. John Lewis Dyer, 1861

The beauty of the mountains, valleys, and hills of South Park are evident to everyone entering or living there. The objective of this book is to examine many of the **Geologic Wonders** of this landscape and explain the nature of their development. Hopefully, knowledge of the geologic evolution of these features will add another dimension to our appreciation and enjoyment of the South Park region.

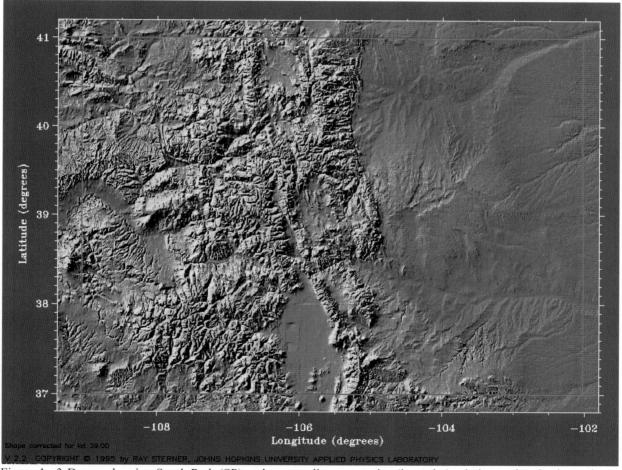

Figure 1. 3-D map showing South Park (SP) and surrounding mountains (lavender) relative to the physiography of Colorado. Copyright 2001 by Ray Sterner, Johns Hopkins University Applied Physics Laboratory. Image reproduced courtesy of Ray Sterner.

Picture yourself sitting on a sandstone outcrop along the **Red Hill hogback** in the middle of the South Park basin. The ridge you are sitting on is one of the **Wonders**. Easily identifiable from space, the history of the east-dipping beach sandstones of this ridge will be described in the chapter that includes discussion of the Cretaceous Period. In each direction, the surrounding mountains have a different geologic origin and age. Clockwise, starting in the west, we see the oldest of the surrounding mountains: the **Mosquito Range**. The rocks you are sitting on are tilted to the east, as are almost all the sedimentary rocks of South Park. The rocks of the basin and the Mosquito Range are **all part of the east flank of a huge anticlinal uplift**, the center of which is west of the Arkansas River in the Sawatch Range. The Mosquito Range is **a series of tilted fault blocks uplifted** along on the east flank of this uplift. In the far distance, Mounts Antero and Princeton are visible. They are located near the middle of the large anticline. The uplift of the Sawatch Anticline was an early event (starting 72 m.y. ago) in the Laramide period of mountain building.

The very prominent **Buffalo Peaks** near the middle of your view to the west are an entirely different story. The upper 1,700 feet of these peaks are **extrusive volcanic rocks** of Middle Tertiary age that apparently filled a large, deep valley. Some of the volcanics came from the west and some may have been of local origin. Since deposition there has been a reversal of topography. Now the hills on either side of the valley have been eroded away and the more erosion-resistant extrusive rocks now stand high as a prominent mountain.

To the northwest and north **along the continental divide** the mountains are the result of the addition of Late Cretaceous, Early Tertiary, and Middle Tertiary **igneous intrusions** into formations that have the east dip common to most rocks of the basin. Some of the intrusions were **stocks** (hardened igneous rocks in the throats of volcanoes.) Other intrusions were **sills** (magma intruded between layers of sedimentary rock), some of which are very hard and now cap mountains such as Mounts Sherman, Bross and Silverheels. Hot waters from the parent magmas, usually during the late stages of intrusive activity, carried the gold, silver, and other minerals that have been exploited in this area.

Swinging our view northeast and east we are looking at the **Front Range**. This uplift was of a different style and was characterized by thrust faults on the east and west sides that made the whole range look like a keystone block in cross section. Part of what you see is the **west flank of the uplift thrust towards you on a shallow ramp over the eastern part of the South Park Basin**. Precambrian rocks were thrust over Early Tertiary rocks in the easternmost part of the basin, which indicates that this stage of mountain building was very late in the Laramide.

In the foreground to the east is **Reinecker Ridge**, which is as high as Red Hill, but of an entirely different character. This ridge contains a unique sequence of **extrusive volcanic rocks.** Welded tuffs and mudflows from a volcano to the north filled a deep north-south valley. Erosion since has removed the softer rocks on either side of the valley so that now the valley fill is the topographic high point. The rocks of this ridge along with those on three other hills west and south of Como are remnants of this extrusive event. The age and source is not known. They may have come from Montgomery Stock immediately north of Mount Silverheels or the Boreas Stock north of Como.

Looking at the south rim of the basin there is a vastly different terrain. **A succession of Middle Tertiary volcanoes extruded mountain-forming piles of volcanic debris.** This outpouring of explosive extrusive rocks **dammed the existing south-flowing stream drainage** to form a **large lake** over the basin and, combined with later tectonic events, caused the drainage (South Platte River) to divert to the east and cross the Front Range at a odd angle. This book's cover picture shows the profile of the youngest of the volcanic events: the **Guffey Volcano.**

Other geologic wonders of South Park are not so obvious and are recognized only after study of the geology in all dimensions. For instance, as you sit on this outcrop, **buried beneath you is the west side of a very old mountain range**. In the subsurface South Park is effectively divided into two entirely different parts by this late Paleozoic event. West of Red Hill there are no Mesozoic or Tertiary sedimentary rocks. East of Red Hill wells drilled for oil and gas found Mesozoic rocks (Morrison and Dakota Formations) lying on Precambrian rocks with no intervening Paleozoic strata.

You can also contemplate the magnitude of the **Wall Mountain Ignimbrite event** 36.73 m.y. ago, which in a day or two incinerated and buried every living thing in a 50-mile wide swath from Mount Aetna northwest of Salida to Castle Rock east of the Front Range.

All of the above and many other geologic wonders of South Park are described in the text and illustrations of the Geologic History chapter and in the Road Logs. Every rock outcrop and the many erosional features that can be identified all have fascinating stories to tell. The Geologic Map, Geologic History Figure 1, is a copy of part of the Geologic Map of Colorado compiled by Ogden Tweto (1979) and published by the US Geological Survey. The accompanying list of symbols (accompanying Geologic History Figure 1) serves the dual functions of identifying exposed rocks and providing a geologic column for the region. The map has a scale of 1:500,000 (about 1 inch = 8 miles). The map shows major drainage, highways, and the township grid.

To avoid bogging down in terminology, I have assumed an elementary knowledge of geology on the part of the reader. A **Glossary** of unusual geologic terms is included. If you haven't had the opportunity to date, it is suggested that you check out freshmen texts on physical and historical geology from the library. I recommend that you skim these texts and read the captions under the figures. These efforts will reward one with the joy of recognizing rock types in road cuts and cliffs wherever you travel and even allow one to speculate on geologic history as you drive by.

This book is divided into a general discussion of the geologic history and economic geology of the South Park region and a series of road logs along major highways and selected county roads. The glossary should help with unfamiliar terms and the list of **Selected References** will prove a jumping off place for further study of this fascinating region.

Acknowledgments

This book is compiled from the contributions of many as reflected in the length of the Selected References. The pioneers were geologists J. Harlan Johnson, J. T. Stark, Ogden Tweto and Quentin D. Singewald. During the 1960's and 1970's Rudy C. Epis and John Chronic directed students from the Colorado School of Mines and the University of Colorado into master's and doctorate theses that discovered many remarkable details of the geologic history. Outstanding among these students are Charles E. Chapin and Richard H. DeVoto, both of whom continue to refine the geologic history of the area and were very generous in sharing their knowledge. Dr. Chapin continues his research on the geology of New Mexico and Colorado and directs students from the New Mexico Institute of Mining and Technology in current thesis projects. Dr. DeVoto is compiling a new geologic map of South Park. John Obradovich of the U. S. Geological Survey supplied a CD with all the radioactive dates obtain in this region. Dean Misantoni, geologist for the Sweet Home Mine, graciously loaned me a copy of a beautifully illustrated publication about the history, geology and crystals of this mine. Craig Barraclough, GIS Coordinator for Park County, has been very generous and cooperative. Every rancher and landowner contacted was most hospitable and always interested in the geology of his or her area.

A very big thanks goes to Douglas and Kathy McGookey. Their help with computers, editing, and enthusiasm for the book has been most gratifying.

Dr. Andrew M. Taylor of Golden, Colorado has recently (1999) written and published a book *Guide to the Geology of Colorado*. This book is written for the layman reader. He generously shared his experience in compiling and self-publishing this book.

Janine Sturdavant generously provided software and expertise that changed all the pictures and drafting to the CMYK format.

Dr. Charles Waggoner has been a long time ally in gathering data and photos.

Like all scientific reports, this book is a progress report reflecting my knowledge to date of the geology and the work of others. New studies, advances in technology, and improvement of sampling techniques are continually providing more geologic information and revising or correcting older concepts.

About the Author

Donald P. McGookey was born and raised in Sandusky, Ohio. He spent two years in the US Navy as an Electronic Technician. A Bachelor's degree was earned from Bowling Green State University, a Master's from the University of Wyoming, and a Ph.D. at The Ohio State University. Texaco Inc. employed him from 1952 to 1979. He worked in various parts of the Rocky Mountains for 17 years and the balance in assignments in New York (International Exploration) and as Chief Geologist in Houston, Texas. Don ended his career with Texaco as manager of exploration in Midland, Texas. Since 1979, he has been an independent geologist working primarily in the Permian Basin of West Texas and southeast New Mexico.

Don's interest in the South Park region began in 1965 with the purchase of 20 acres four miles northwest of Fairplay. After putting six children through college the McGookeys were able in 1989 to finally build a small cabin on the acreage. The view from the cabin is from a substage terminal moraine across a park at the central part of the Mosquito Range. Thus, much of the geologic column is visible from the cabin, plus the 20 acres is strewn with samples (cobbles and boulders) from the mountains that were transported there by glaciers. From 1965 to the present, Don collected books on the geology of South Park and lectured locally on lode and placer gold, glaciation and the Guffey Volcano.

The research for this book has updated and expanded his knowledge of the South Park Region, allowed the recognition of the Geologic Wonders that resulted in great scenery and, hopefully, resulted in a book that others will enjoy.

Figure 2. Mosquito Creek Road Log MP 7.2.
Boulder is Silver Plume Granite from Treasurevault Stock.

Geologic History

Summary of Geologic History

The geologic history of an area such as the South Park region is read from the succession of rocks exposed at the surface and present in the subsurface. The record in South Park, like every other land area in the world, is cyclic and inherently incomplete. Each cycle includes (1) long periods of deposition of sediments followed by (2) periods of igneous activity and/or mountain building, which in turn are followed or accompanied by (3) a long period of erosion that removes part or all of the previous record. Study of the maps and cross sections in this book will illustrate several of these cycles in the rock record of South Park.

The rock record in the South Park Region spans 1,800+ million years. Two-thirds of that time was in the Precambrian. In the early part of this time, Colorado was an area of small island microcontinents (like present day Madagascar or Corsica) with intervening deep ocean troughs where sands and shales were deposited. By plate-to-plate collision, these island microcontinents were successively welded to an older core area of the continent that extended from Wyoming to the Ontario Province of Canada. By the end of the Precambrian, all of Colorado was a part of the North American continent and has remained so.

The Early and Middle Paleozoic were characterized by (1) repeated flooding of this part of the continent by tropical marine waters and (2) little tectonic activity. During the Late Paleozoic, the pattern changed dramatically. The western half of the South Park region was involved in a broad northwest trending trough while the eastern half was uplifted into low relief mountains where erosion removed all of the earlier Paleozoic cover and cut deeply into Precambrian rocks. There followed a long period during the Early Mesozoic with erosion and no record of deposition in the South Park region. Late Jurassic continental deposits are preserved over the eastern half of South Park followed by marine flooding of the area near the middle of the Cretaceous Period. From about 100 to 70 million years ago, the whole state of Colorado was part of a regional depression of the central part of the continent so that a significant thickness of Cretaceous marine mud and sand was deposited. Towards the end of the Cretaceous, the sea withdrew eastward and the area has remained above sea level.

About the time of the sea withdrawal (and probably the cause) the initial broad uplifts of the long Laramide episode of mountain building (orogeny) began in parts of Colorado. The area of South Park was on the eastern side (flank) of a very broad uplift that centered on the Sawatch Range west of Buena Vista. The Laramide Orogeny was a series of mountain-building pulses that continued from the Late Cretaceous through the Early Tertiary Periods, roughly from 72 to 40 m.y. ago.

Explanation of Geologic Map and Geologic Column for South Park Region

Scale: 1:500,000, 1"=approx. 8 miles. Township grid is 6 miles on each side.
Map shows exposed rocks, drainage, major roads, towns and 500-foot topographic contours
Source: Geologic Map of Colorado, Ogden Tweto, 1979, published by the U.S. Geological Survey

Stratigraphic Column		
Age	**Symbol**	**Identification**
Quaternary (1.6 m.y. to present)		
	Qa	Unconsolidated modern alluvium
	Qg	Glacial gravels and alluvium
	Qd	Older glacial gravels and alluvium.
	Qgo	Older Gravels and Alluvium
Tertiary (65 to 1.6 m.y.)		
	Td	Dry Union Formation. Includes Wagontongue Formation (Miocene)
	Tos Antero	Oligocene Sedimentary Rocks. Includes Florissant Lake Beds and Formation (lakebeds and volcanic deposits).
	Te	Eocene Prevolcanic Sedimentary Rocks. Echo Park Alluvium
	Tsp	South Park Formation. Arkosic sandstone and shale, volcanoclastic conglomerate, flows and breccia.
Igneous Rocks of Tertiary Age		
	Tbb	Basalt Flows. Age (3.5-26 m.y.)
	Tial	Andesitic mud flows and tuffs.
	Tpl	Andesite lavas, breccias, tuffs and conglomerates. (General age 30-35 m.y.)
	Tmi	Middle Tertiary intrusive rocks. (Age 20-40 m.y.)
	Twm	Wall Mountain Ignimbrite. (36.73 m.y.)
Igneous Rocks of Late Cretaceous and Early Tertiary Age		
	TKi	Laramide Intrusive Rocks. (Age 72-50 m.y.)
Sedimentary Rocks of Cretaceous Age. (146 to 65 m.y.)		
	Klf	Laramie and Fox Hills Formations
	Kf	Fox Hills Formation
	Kp	Pierre Shale
	Kc	Colorado Group
	Kd	Dakota Group
Sedimentary Rocks of Jurassic (208 to 146 m.y.) and Cretaceous Ages		
	KJde	Dakota, Morrison and Garo Formations
Sedimentary Rocks of Permian and Pennsylvanian Ages (323 to 245 m.y.)		
	PPm	Maroon Formation
Sedimentary Rocks of Pennsylvanian Age (323 to 290 m.y.)		
	Pm	Minturn Formation
	Pmb	Minturn and Belden Formations
	Pmbe	Evaporitic facies of Minturn and Belden Formations.
Sedimentary Rocks of Pre-Pennsylvanian Paleozoic Age (Lower Paleozoic Rocks, 570 to 323 m.y.)		
	MC	Leadville, Dyer, Manitou, Peerless and Sawatch Formations
	MDO	Leadville, Dyer and Manitou Formations.
Igneous Rocks of Precambrian Age		
	Yp	Rocks of Pikes Peak Batholith. (1,000 m.y.)
	Yg	Granitic Rocks of 1400 m.y. Age Group. Includes Silver Plum, Sherman and Cripple Creek Granites.
	Yam	Alkalic and mafic Rocks in small plutons.
	Xg	Granitic Rocks of 1700 m.y. Age Group. (Age 1650-1730 m.y.)
Metamorphic Rocks of Precambrian Age (Age 1700-1800 m.y.)		
	Xb	Biotitic gneiss, schist and migmatite.
	Xfh	Felsic and hornblende gneisses, quartzite, conglomerate and interlayered mica schist.

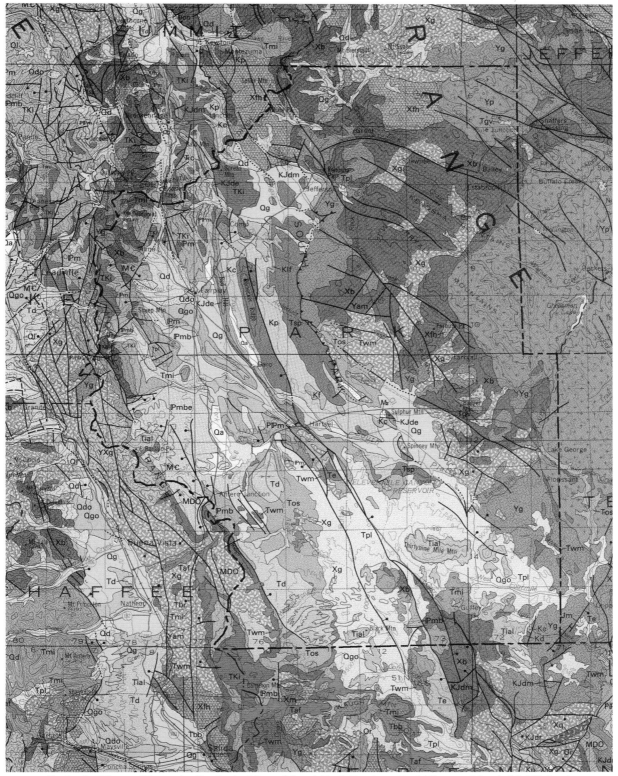

Geologic History Figure 1. Geologic Map of South Park Region. Park County Line is highlighted.

A short time later in the Late Cretaceous, uplift of the Front Range started, providing two sides to the basin. Contemporaneously, igneous intrusions in a broad northeast-trending belt from the Telluride to the Boulder area, the Colorado Mineral Belt, added to the mountain building (and mineral-wealth) of Colorado. This belt of igneous intrusions crosses the northwestern part of the South Park region and provided the hard resistant rocks that cap mountains along the Continental Divide. Volcanic debris from the igneous centers covered much of the South Park region, but most was removed by extensive erosion that reduced the area to one of low relief by the end of the Eocene. By the end of the Laramide Orogeny in late Eocene time, the basin had three sides and drained to the south.

A complete change to the region occurred during Oligocene and early Miocene time. There was new intrusive and extrusive activity in the Colorado Mineral Belt. At the same time, extensive piles of explosive volcanic debris from several eruptive centers created volcanoes across the southern part of the region. Mudflows from these volcanoes dammed the south-flowing drainage and created a large lake that may have covered all of South Park. This lake is contemporaneous with the better-known Oligocene lake in the Florissant valley. The present course of the South Platte River across the Front Range is the result of drainage from this lake.

The Late Tertiary Miocene and Pliocene stages (25-2 m.y. ago) again were times of mountain building. The entire area was epierogenically uplifted, possibly as much as 5,000 feet. Old faults were rejuvenated and new fault blocks were created. The combination of broad epierogenic and local fault block movements formed the mountains being eroded today.

During the Pleistocene (last two m.y.), repeated cycles of extreme climatic change caused periodic regional cooling and the development of glaciers in the valleys above 10,000 feet. Younger glacial activity tends to erase the evidence of older glaciers, but at least three periods of glaciation are clearly recorded. The glacial activity eroded and redistributed (transported) considerable gold, resulting in placer deposits in several northwestern valleys. There is some evidence that the Late Tertiary uplifting continued into the Pleistocene and may still be in progress. The absence of earthquakes would indicate it is not, but then one never knows.

Precambrian

Precambrian time covers the history of the earth from the formation of the planet, about 4.6 billion years ago, to 570 million years ago. The rocks in Colorado record part of the later half of the Precambrian. Rocks of the older Archean Era (4.6 to 2.5 billion years ago) are present to the north across much of Wyoming. The Precambrian section of Colorado presents rocks that were added by plate tectonics to the Wyoming core area during the Proterozoic Era (2,500 to 570 m.y.). In the South Park region, the oldest rocks include a middle Proterozoic (2,000 to 1,800 million years ago) period of volcanic activity and a long period of sedimentation in deep marine troughs. This section was extensively recrystallized by regional metamorphism at about 1,775 million years ago and further metamorphosed by contact with intrusion of the first of a series of granite batholiths at about 1,700 million years. The metasedimentary gneisses are principally biotite gneisses, consisting of plagioclase, quartz, and biotite (Tweto, 1980a). Minor layers include quartzites and impure marbles. The metavolcanic gneisses consist of two types, one being amphibolite or hornblende gneiss and the other quartzofeldspathic gneiss. The foliation (banding) and complex folding common in all gneisses allows easy identification of this rock type, even in small pebbles.

Igneous Rocks of ~1,700 Million Year age

Igneous rocks of the earlier period of batholithic intrusions range in age from 1,730-1,650 m.y. The event included mountain building and is named the **Boulder Creek Orogeny**. Batholithic intrusions of this age are present in both the Mosquito and Front Ranges. The rock type is primarily granite, but may include more basic rocks. Some exhibit a distinctive porphyritic texture where very large plagioclase crystals are surrounded by a course equagranular granite texture.

Igneous Rocks of ~1,400 m.y. age

Granite intrusives ranging in age from 1,480 to 1,350 m.y. occur widely in the Precambrian terrains as many small intrusive bodies. The **Silver Plume Granite** of the Idaho Springs area is recognized as typical of this group. They lack foliation and are commonly discordant with earlier granites or gneisses. (Please see mile point 7.0 of Mosquito Creek Road Log.)

Igneous Rocks of ~1,000 m.y. age

These rocks dominate the southeast part of the South Park Region and are named the **Pikes Peak Granite**. This very large batholith covers much of the southern part of the Front Range and has an age of 1,040 m.y. Several types of granite can be seen, but most commonly it is equagranular granite that is course-grained and pink to pale orange.

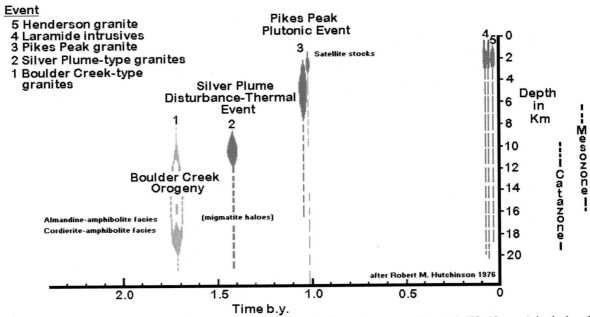

Geologic History Figure 2. Plutonic events vs. depth-zone of emplacement. Event 4 (72-40 m.y.) includes the gold and silver-bearing intrusives of the Leadville, London Mountain and Alma Districts. Event 5 (30-28 m.y.) includes the Climax Stock, emplacement of the rhodochrosite suite of minerals around the Buckskin Stock and volcanic activity and mineral emplacement in the Cripple Creek area (After Hutchison, 1976).

The erosional surface (so-called Great Unconformity) at the top of Precambrian rocks is exposed in many parts of the South Park region. Regardless of the age of the overlying beds be they Early Paleozoic, Late Paleozoic, Jurassic, or Tertiary in age, the top of the Precambrian is a sharp contact that is easily identified. The metamorphic gneisses and various granites generally are hard and commonly found as individual samples in gravel to boulder-size rocks deposited by glaciers or streams. Study of the different types at the outcrop in valley walls or road cuts often will allow identification of that same rock when it is far from home.

Paleozoic Rocks

Sediments of Paleozoic age are found only over the western third of Park County. The relatively thin section (about 1,000 feet) that is pre-Pennsylvanian in age contains sandstone and carbonate sections of Late Cambrian, Ordovician, Devonian, and Mississippian age. Where exposed along the east side of the Mosquito Range in canyon and cirque walls (e.g. three miles south of Trout Creek Pass and the east side of Horseshoe Mountain) the hard sandstones and dolomites present imposing cliffs. The carbonates play an important role in mineral deposition.

The Pennsylvanian and Permian section is very thick in the Antero Reservoir area. The section is almost all clastic sediments deposited in a broad northwest trending trough. They are derived from a newly uplifted mountain range to the east called the Ancestral Front Range. Along with the Uncompahgria Range of southwestern Colorado, these two trends made up the mountain systems of the Late Paleozoic Ancestral Rockies. The center of the

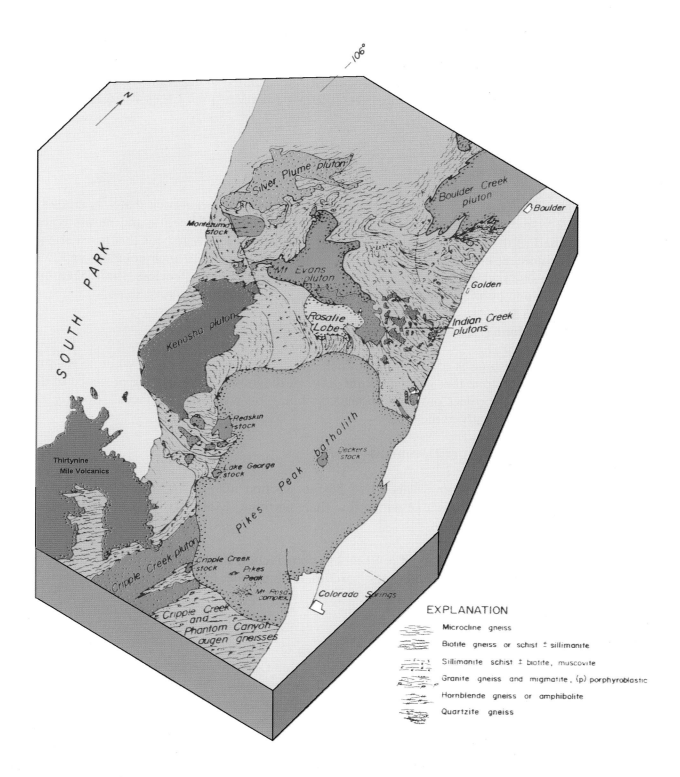

Geologic History Figure 3. Plutons of the central Front Range (after Hutchison, 1976).

north-northwest trending Ancestral Front Range was about the western edge of the present Front Range. The western edge trended north south at about the middle of South Park. The eastern side was about the middle of the present day Front Range. R. H. DeVoto (1971) provides an excellent discussion of Paleozoic stratigraphy complete with distribution maps for each period. The following discussion is taken principally from Q. D. Singewald and B. S. Butler's (1941) discussion of the stratigraphy in the vicinity of the London Fault. Please compare this discussion with the figures accompanying the Mosquito Creek Road Log.

Pre-Pennsylvanian

Sawatch Quartzite (Upper Cambrian)

The Sawatch Quartzite was deposited upon a surface of Precambrian rock that was eroded to a remarkably smooth plain. The formation is easily recognized by white and purple colors. The lower half of the formation is a 60 to 115-foot section of quartzite beds that resist erosion and form prominent cliffs. The base of the formation is an 8 to 12 inch conglomerate with pebbles up to one inch in diameter. The 35 to 62-foot upper half (**Peerless Shale Member**) includes white and purple quartzites, limestone intervals, and grayish-green shale.

Manitou Limestone (Lower Ordovician)

The Manitou Limestone is 95 to 190 feet thick and consists of thin-bedded white to medium blue dolomitic limestone that weathers light gray. A diagnostic feature is the presence of thin siliceous bands that project out as pronounced ribbing on weathered surfaces. Locally, the formation is slightly shaly at the top.

Chaffee Formation (Upper Devonian)

Parting Quartzite Member. This 21 to 55-foot section may be brownish-gray quartzite, limy quartzite, or sandy limestone with a few shale partings. Most beds are cross-bedded and conglomeratic.

Dyer Dolomite Member. This is a 40 to 115-foot section of alternating creamy and white dolomitic limestone that is sometimes hard to differentiate from the overlying Leadville Limestone.

Leadville Limestone (Mississippian).

Above an erosional unconformity at top of the Dyer Dolomite is a 2 to 12-foot sandstone. This unit is in turn overlain by a conspicuous limestone breccia that is two to five feet thick. The rest of the 115 to 168-foot formation is a massive dark blue to black, dense to very fine-grained dolomitic limestone. Black chert nodules and streaks are common. The weathered limestone has extremely pitted surfaces. Throughout the formation so-called "zebra rock" is common. This is limestone that has been crystallized and partly replaced by veinlets of white dolomite that give the rock a striped appearance.

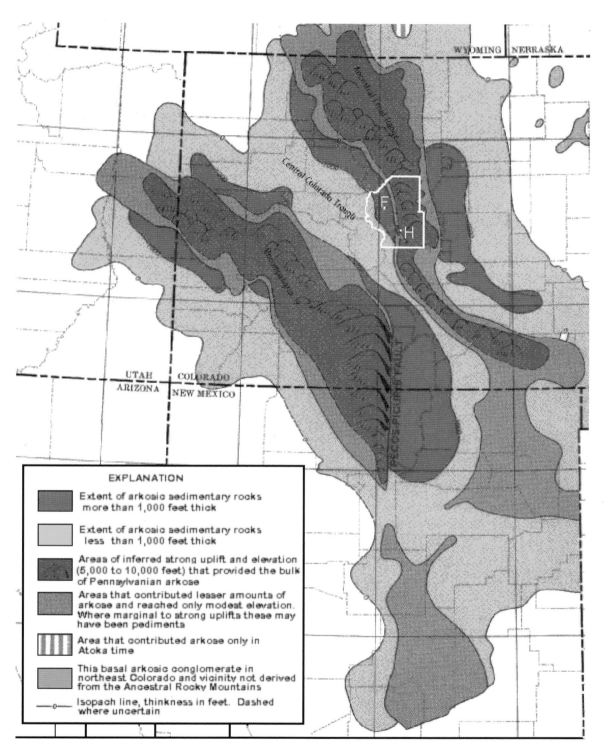

Geologic History Figure 4. Pennsylvanian-Permian Ancestral Rocky Mountains and Central Colorado Trough. F=Fairplay, H= Hartsel, Park County is outlined in white. After Mallory, 1972.

Pennsylvanian and Permian

The first sediments overlying the Leadville Limestone may be a regolith (old soil, lag boulders, etc.) section up to 68 feet thick. In most of the Mosquito Range the Early Pennsylvanian sediments are marine black shales of the **Belding Formation**. They form an easily recognized sequence overlying the Leadville Limestone and underlying (and in some places grading upward into) the fluvial red sandstones, shales and conglomerates of the **Maroon Formation**. The proximity to land of the Belding Shales is shown by the lateral gradation into fluvial and deltaic (swamp) sediments called the **Minturn Formation (Weber Sandstone** of older publications) in the northern part of the Mosquito Range (DeVoto, 1980b). Occasionally, slightly flattened trunks of scale trees (tree ferns common in the Pennsylvanian) can be found in the Belding and Minturn Formations. The direction of facies change and the type of material indicate that the initial uplift of the Ancestral Front Range was starting at this time and sediment was being transported from east to west into the Colorado Trough.

As the uplift continued a marine seaway was present in the central part of the Colorado Trough (Minturn Formation). Laterally to the east the sediments were courser and red indicating a lateral change to fluvial and piedmont sedimentation. During part of the time communication with the sea became restricted and the evaporite rocks gypsum and salt were deposited. (During all of Pennsylvanian time, South Park was just a few degrees north of the Equator.) Most of the evaporite deposition was to the northwest in Eagle County, but deposits in the western part of South Park were thick enough to result in salt-flowage structures north of Antero Junction. There was a salt works during the late 1800's along Salt Creek between East and West Hall Buttes. From the middle of Pennsylvanian and possibly continuing into Permian time, only Maroon Formation red beds were deposited in South Park. The flood of sedimentation contemporaneous with uplift of the Ancestral Front Range resulted in a total thickness of Pennsylvanian (and Permian?) strata that may exceed 10,000 feet in the Antero-Leadville area.

Mesozoic-Early Cenozoic

There is no record for the period from the middle Permian to the late Jurassic. The geologic history of the South Park Region after the Paleozoic is completely different in types of rocks deposited.

The first deposit overlying the Paleozoic Maroon Formation is the **Garo Sandstone**. This red to gray sandstone is the western ridge or bench of Red Hill, a ridge that runs north to south through the middle of South Park. The beds of this medium to fine-grained sandstone are massive with large-scale cross bedding, suggesting an eolian origin in part (please see Highway 285 Road Log Figure 12). In a few areas the basal beds are conglomeratic. The type locality is a ghost town about halfway between Fairplay and Hartzell where the beds of sand are about 409 feet thick. It pinches out south of Hartsel and thins to 132 feet at Red Hill Pass. The sandstone lies unconformably on the Maroon Formation and also on the Precambrian near Hartzell where the Maroon is absent. There is a disconformity between the

Garo and the Morrison Formations. No fossils have been found, so the age of the Garo Sandstone is unknown.

The **Morrison Formation** occurs in narrow outcrops along the west side of Red Hill. East of Hartsel there are several outcrops where the Morrison is deposited on the Precambrian surface. The Morrison Formation is famous for dinosaur remains in northwest Colorado and southern Wyoming. To date, only fragments of bone and fresh water invertebrate fossils have been found in South Park. The formation consists of shale, with some beds of limestone, siltstone, sandstone and lenses (up to 10 feet thick) of conglomerate. The lower half is predominantly light shades of gray, green and cream; the upper part is red, brown, mottle red and green and yellow. The thickness ranges from 250 to 360 feet. The assignment of this section to the late Jurassic Morrison Formation is based on its similarity to the section at the type locality along the east side of the Front Range.

The outcrops of the east-dipping Cretaceous **Dakota Group** sandstones form the highest part of a north-south hogback (Red Hill) that is a dominant topographic feature of the middle of South Park. Measured sections at Red Hill pass, Hartsel, and Sulphur Mountain are featured in a discussion of the Dakota Group by R. J. Weimer (1970). In most localities, the Dakota is essentially a soft white to light gray sandstone. It weathers to buff to yellowish brown and has an average thickness of 225 feet (please see Highway 285 Road Log Figure 13). These are the near-shore and beach sandstones deposited during the first submerging of this area by the Cretaceous Western Interior Sea in Early Cretaceous time.

The overlying section is a sequence of shallow and deepwater marine deposits that is predominantly black shale with some limestones. It was deposited along the west side of a seaway (an epicontinental sea) that extended across North America from the Gulf of Mexico to the Arctic Ocean (McGookey, 1972). Mapping by Stark, et al, 1949 divided the South Park shale section into a lower Benton Shale, Niobrara Formation, and Pierre Formation.

The 410 to 460-foot **Benton Shale** conformably overlies the Dakota Group along the eastern side of the Dakota hogback. Invertebrate fossils (oysters and ammonites) indicate an early Late Cretaceous age. Thin beds of bentonite are common. These altered volcanic ash beds probably came from volcanoes of the Sierra Nevada or Idaho batholiths.

The **Niobrara Formation** crops out along the eastern side of the Dakota hogback. The average thickness is 540 feet. The formation has two divisions, a lower chalky limestone (40-70 feet) and upper calcareous shale. Topographically, the lower limestone may form a low ridge and locally has been quarried for lime.

The **Pierre Shale** crops out in many valley areas east of the Dakota hogback, such as along Trout Creek between Red Hill and Reinecker Ridge and the broad, topographically low area along the South Platte River east of Hartsel. It is estimated to be 2,300 to 2,700 feet thick. The formation consists of black fissile shale with some sandy and calcareous beds. At 250 to 300 feet above the base there is a section of sandy beds that yielded a small quantity of oil in a well drilled north of Hartsel (Stark et al, 1949). At the top of the formation there is a gradual transition from shale through sandy shale to sandstone of the Fox Hills Formation.

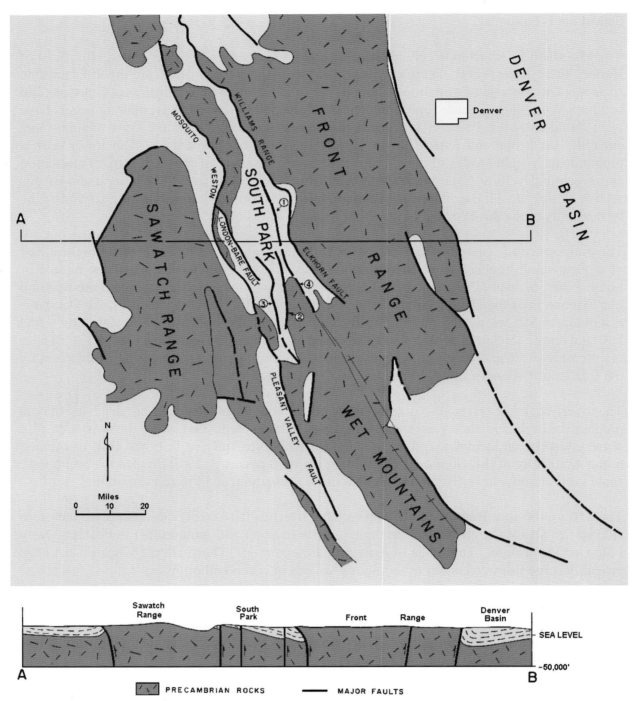

Geologic History Figure 5. Tectonic setting of South Park and index to major faults. Most of these faults were progressively developed from west to east during the Laramide Orogeny and later rejuvenated during the Miocene. (1) South Park Fault; (2) Agate Creek Fault; (3) Antero Reservoir Fault; (4) Current Creek Fault. After DeVoto, 1971.

The retreat of the Cretaceous epicontinental sea from this area was expedited by the Sawatch Range uplift and is recorded by the change from Pierre Shale deposition progressively to Fox Hills beach sandstones and then to **Laramie** non-marine sediments and volcanic deposits.

Box 1.
Laramide Orogeny

Orogenies are periods of mountain building and basin formation. They include large and small scale folding of the rock strata, faulting, igneous activity and accelerated erosion of the uplifted terrains.

The Laramide orogeny affected the entire South Park region. Prior to the first pulse of tectonic movement a thick undisturbed blanket 5,000 to 10,000 feet thick of Cretaceous sandstones and shales and minor older Mesozoic sedimentary rocks covered the area. The event that marked the onset of the Laramide at South Park was the uplift of the very large **Sawatch anticline** starting 72 m.y. ago. Faults on the east and northeast flanks of this anticline defined the structure of the mountains of the Mosquito Range. The **east flank of the Sawatch anticline extended across the entire area** providing a prevailing (approximately 20 degrees) east dip to all pre-Oligocene sediments of South Park.

The next major events were repeated igneous stock and sill intrusions of the **Colorado Mineral Belt** during the period from 70 to 40 m.y. ago. Volcanoes above the intrusions contributed pyroclastic debris and mudflows that interbed with contemporaneous sediment deposition. During this activity, the **Front Range** was uplifted (starting about 70 m.y. ago and continuing into the Tertiary). This uplift dragged the sediments of the east side of the basin upward forming the deep **Mexican Ridge syncline** in the easternmost part of South Park. Late in the Laramide, part of the west flank of the Front Range was thrust (**Elkhorn Thrust**) over the east part of South Park.

The **Fox Hills Formation** crops out around the north and west sides of the Mexican Ridge syncline that dominates the eastern part of the South Park Basin, and also around the south plunge of the anticline east of Hartsel in T.11 and 12 South, R. 75 W. The formation generally is not well exposed. It is primarily a white to brown, poorly cemented, loose sand. Cross bedding is common. Concretions are numerous locally, some being large. The maximum thickness is about 350 feet. This formation consists of beach and near-shore sand deposited during the final withdrawal of the Interior Sea from this part of Colorado.

The last sediments deposited in the basin during the Cretaceous Period are fluvial, swamp and lake deposits of the **Laramie Formation**. Outcrops are restricted to the northeast part of South Park near Jefferson and Como. Outcrops are poor as the formation has few resistant beds. Brown to black shale and volcanic tuff are dominant along with white to dark gray sandstones and coal. At Peabody Switch, four miles northwest of Como, the formation has been folded and metamorphosed to a quartzite by contact with the Boreas Stock.

Contemporaneous with the deposition of the Laramie Formation a series of major igneous events occurred in the Leadville-London Mountain-Alma-Tarryall areas. Most of the mineral deposits (including gold and silver) were precipitated from hydrothermal waters during the late stages of each intrusive event. Meanwhile, out in the basin, swamp conditions prevailed part of the time and resulted in the deposition of three coal beds. The first is near the base of the Laramie Formation and is from six to eight feet thick at the King Mine three miles southeast of Como. The second is 180 feet higher and has a thickness of one and a half to four feet. The third is 220 above the first and is reported to be four feet thick. These coals were mined in the late 1800's.

The maximum reported thickness of the Laramie Formation is 375 feet. The formation was eroded and even completely removed in many areas prior to the deposition of the overlying South Park Formation.

Tertiary Sediments

Significant changes are recorded in the sediments and volcanic rocks of the **South Park (formerly Denver) Formation.** These rocks overly Pierre to Laramie sections with low angle unconformity. They are restricted to the large **Mexican Ridge syncline**. The formation consists of conglomerate, gravel, and sandstone interbedded with volcanic tuff, mudflows, and debris flows directly from the flanks of volcanoes. The throat of a large volcano, the **Boreas Stock**, is located five miles north-northwest of Como. Radioactive dates of 44 to 41 m.y. have been obtained from rocks of this stock, which is traversed from two miles north of Como to the Boreas Pass. Igneous activity also continued in the Leadville and probably in the London Mountain and Alma areas to the northwest and west.

Particle in the sandstones and conglomerates also identify source areas from Precambrian rocks. Granite boulders and pebbles and arkosic grits in the sands are very common, especially in the upper part of the South Park Formation. The formation has an estimated maximum thickness of 8,000 feet. It is measured at 6,300 feet south of the King Mine and thins to 1,300 feet near Hartsel. It is not known whether the thinning is caused by distance from the source or erosion. Fossil wood and leaves have been collected at many locations that indicate an early Tertiary age.

The South Park Formation mapped at **Reinecker Ridge** is especially notable as it consists of extrusive rocks deposited in a north-south valley from a volcano to the north. A basal section of welded tuffs (ignimbrites) is overlain by about 500 feet of mudflow agglomerates. The age of the Reinecker Ridge volcanics is in question. They may be Late Eocene or Oligocene rather than Paleocene-Eocene as currently mapped.

Sometime during the Eocene, the west side of the Front Range was thrust westward for several miles over South Park Formation beds of the east side of the Mexican Ridge syncline along the low angle **Elkhorn Thrust**. Following this event, the area had a **long history of erosion that resulted in low relief hills and fairly wide valleys and basins** by the end of the Eocene. At the end of the Eocene, all drainage of South Park exited to the south through the area now occupied by the Oligocene volcanic pile.

Geologic History Figure 6. Aerial view looking south at US Highway 285 across Red Hill Pass. From right to left: west slope on Maroon Formation; first road cut is Garo Sandstone; grassy area covers the Morrison Formation and highest crest of hill is outcrop of Dakota Sandstone East (left) of the Dakota hogback. Benton Shale and Niobrara Limestone are grass-covered in this view.

Geologic History Figure 7. Mudflow deposits in the Laramie Formation east of Reinecker Ridge.

Post-Eocene Geologic History

Post-Laramide, Late Eocene Erosion Surface

All of the Laramide tectonic mountain-building activities terminated by mid-Eocene and were followed by a long period of erosion. The area was reduced to one of **broad valleys and low relief by the end of the Eocene** (Epis and Chapin, 1975, Chapin and Kelley, 1997). Rivers drained from west, north and east into the South Park Basin. The resulting major drainage systems exited to the south through valleys near the present Current-Tallahassee Creeks and Fourmile Creek that eventually flow eastward through the Canon City embayment of the east front of the Rockies.

Remnants of the **late Eocene surface** can be seen in the low relief of the crest of the southern Front Range and Rampart Range between Colorado Springs and Denver. The surface cuts across rocks of varying hardness, and is equally well developed in the east part of the South Park Basin. The Elkhorn Upland is part of the late Eocene surface. This late Eocene period of low relief is found in places throughout the Rocky Mountains. The mountains we see today are the result of mid and late Tertiary volcanism and uplift, and some uplift may be still occurring.

In Park County, the deposit immediately overlying the late Eocene surface is the **Wall Mountain Tuff**. This extrusive volcanic deposit originated 36.73 +/-0.07 m.y. ago from a volcano overlying the southern part of the Mount Princeton batholith in the Sawatch Range southwest of Buena Vista. It is a rhyolitic tuff that can be traced a minimum of 100 miles east to the Castle Rock area south of Denver (Geologic History Figure 8). Over its extent the Wall Mountain tuff is welded, which indicates that it was deposited from a dense hot cloud (>700 degrees Centigrade, called a "Nuee Ardente") of hot gas, ash and fine crystals hugging the ground and flowing eastward at great velocity (estimated at 225 miles per hour 31 miles from source). It vaporized every living thing it touched. The cloud moved downhill from the Mount Aetna area with enough momentum to flow over the low divide east of South Park and onto the slopes east of the Front Range. No eruption of this immense size has ever been observed. As the cloud slows, the liquid and solid components, still red-hot, settle and blanket the topography with the valleys receiving the thickest mantles. As the cloud settles, the hot glass particles touch and weld. The resulting welded tuff is a hard, cliff-forming rock called an "ignimbrite".

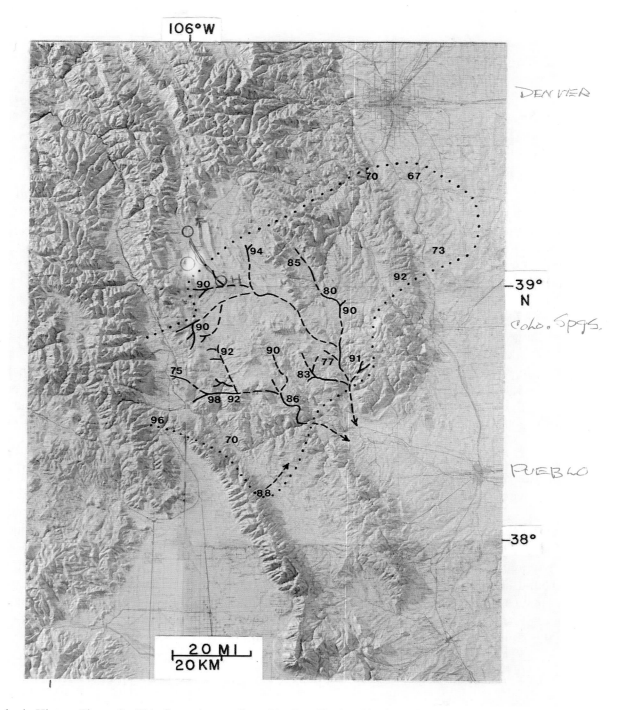

Geologic History Figure 8. This figure is contributed by Dr. Charles Chapin. The base is a composite of Army Relief maps (two degree quadrangles) and shows the late Eocene drainage of South Park. Known paleovalleys are shown with solid and dashed lines. The dotted line shows the extent of the Wall Mountain Tuff based on outcrops. The Wall Mountain Tuff is thicker in the Late Eocene valleys and lies on a conglomerate in the valleys Thus the base of the combined sections defines the valleys. The numbers represent present elevations in hundreds of feet of the base of the Wall Mountain Tuff, which lies on the late Eocene surface. Please see Epis and Chapin, 1975 for additional discussion of this surface.

Oligocene Volcanic Activity

Thirtynine Mile Volcanic Field

This very large volcanic pile covers much of the southern part of the South Park region and provides the spectacular profile shown on the cover of this book. It was built by a succession of different types of volcanic rocks extruded (and minor intrusive dikes) from 33 to 29 m.y. ago. Contemporaneous volcanic activity occurred to the south at Silver Cliff and Rosita and near the northern end of the San Luis Valley that is associated with the northeast part of the San Juan volcanic field (Steven, 1975).

Geologic History Figure 9. Aerial view across west end of Guffey Caldera. Hammond Peak is five miles north of the first volcanic center that is the West Antelope Mountain Center. Thirty-one Mile Mountain is the second volcanic center.

For the Thirtynine Mile volcanic field **four successive source areas** have been mapped (Epis and Chapin, 1968). The first is centered at **Antelope Mountain** five miles southwest of Guffey. The second is centered at **Thirtyone Mile Mountain** three miles southwest of Guffey. The third and largest source area was the **Guffey center**. The last center was at **Waugh Mountain** about 13 miles southwest of Guffey. The flanks of the Guffey volcano can be easily viewed from many points in the northern part of South Park. They include the west slope of Black Mountain (dips eight degrees west), the north slope at Thirtynine Mile Mountain (10 to 15 degrees north), and part of the east slope at Saddle Mountain (northeast dip). Castle, McIntyre, and Witcher Mountains east of Guffey all show two to six degrees east dip of the east flank. Dips of the south slope of the volcano are less than those reported above.

Box 2. Thirtynine Mile Volcanic Field Extrusive Centers and sequence of events. Listed from youngest to oldest.

Fear Creek Conglomerate with Fish Creek Tuff (27.83 m.y.) from San Juan Volcanic Field

Upper Andesite. This is the youngest extrusive formation of the Thirtynine Mile field. Forms high slopes of **Waugh Mountain** above 9,800 feet. Basalt and andesite flows and flow breccias with minor tuffs. Probably came from fissures in Waugh Mountain and is 300 to 1,200 feet thick in that area.

Waugh Mountain Center. Several domes, necks and dikes of latitic to rhyolitic composition along pre-volcanic faults

Ash Flow 7 (includes five flows that give a bench-like topography west of Waugh Mountain)

Ash Flow 6 is the same as the **Gribbles Park Tuff (32.9 m.y.)**

Ash Flow 5, Antero Formation and Lake Florissant. The Antero Formation has an Upper Course Sandstone and Conglomerate Member (1,300 feet) and a Lower Tuff and Limestone Member (2,000 feet 33.65 to 33.71 m.y.)

Ash Flow 4 is the same as the **Agate Creek Tuff.**

Guffey Center of Thirtynine Mile Volcanic Field. Upper Andesite laharic breccia member has well-stratified andesitic to basaltic lava flows, laharic breccias and minor ash-fall tuffs. Mudflow rocks predominate and dip four to ten degrees away from Guffey Center. The unit is 2,000 feet thick on Thirtynine Mile Mountain. These rocks represent erosional flanks of a large composite volcano (Guffey Volcano). Basal diameters were ten miles north to south and 16 miles east to west. The dimensions of this volcano are of the same order as those of the large volcanic cones of the Middle Cascade Mountain in Oregon and Washington (Epis and Chapin, 1968). Collapse of the caldera probably occurred (possibly more than once) during extrusion of the Upper Andesite Member. There are several intrusive necks or stocks six miles west of Guffey along the southwest and west side of the collapse ring including Hammond Peak, Baldy Mountain and Gold Hill. Epis and Chapin, 1968, identify these conduits as major feeds in the building of the Guffey Volcano.

Lower Andesite (34.1 m.y.) Numerous small vents around field erupted intermediate laharic breccias up to 500 feet thick over 800 square miles. **Ash flow 3** remnants in lower 200 feet.

Thirtyone Mile Center. This 1,200-foot hornblende andesite dome tilts flows from Antelope Center and intrudes basic to intermediate flows, tuffs, and breccias derived from that center. Thirtyone Mile Center covers eight to ten square miles.

West Antelope Mountain Center is an 800-foot high lava dome with extrusive ash, pumice and tuff) that covers three square miles.

Tallahassee Creek Conglomerate. Arkose plus fragments of Wall Mountain Tuff.

Stirrup Ranch Tuff (36.67 m.y.)

Wall Mountain Tuff (36.73 m.y.)

Prevolcanic Arkose. (Balfour Formation of DeVoto, 1971). **Valley-fill in Late Eocene surface.**

Geologic History Figure 10. 3-D look at Guffey Caldera (third volcanic center of the Thirtynine Mile Volcanic Field). 39MM-Thirtynine Mile Mountain (north flank of volcano), BM-black Mountain (southwest flank of volcano), WA-West Antelope Mountain (first volcanic center), 31MM-Thirty-one Mile Mountain (second volcanic center). Waugh Mountains are the fourth and youngest volcanic center. The ten mile long caldera is outlined in red. Peaks west-northwest of Guffey within the collapse area are post-collapse intrusives of the Chumway Park area. Copyright 2001 by Ray Sterner, Johns Hopkins University Applied Physics Laboratory.

The caldera that resulted from the collapse of the central part of the Guffey volcano is five by ten miles. Baldy Mountain and Hammond Peak are examples of stocks (throats of volcanoes) that developed in the Chumway Park area of the western part of the caldera sometime after the collapse.

Most of the extrusive rocks from the volcanoes are intermediate to acidic in chemical composition. Typical of this type of volcano, most of the activity was explosive venting of ash and volcanic bombs. The slopes are composed primarily of mudflows with seven interbedded ignimbrites from a volcano to the west. Usually the ignimbrites stand out from the dark gray mudflows as they are a lighter color (sometime cream-colored) and more resistant to erosion. The internal lineup of crystals in ignimbrites records the direction of flow (Please see Guffey Road Log Figure 3.)

Southeast from Hartsel Colorado 9 traverses mudflow deposits and climbs 16 miles to the center of the volcano two miles northwest of Guffey. Study of the deposits in road cuts along the highway or on county roads shows dark gray chaotic deposits of large and small rocks in a matrix of gray ash that was turned to mud. The boulder and cobble-size rocks were originally blown out of the volcano as volcanic bombs. This type of deposit is common to explosive volcanoes. During eruptions ejected bombs and ash rain on the high slopes of the volcano, and after heavy rains are mobilized to flow down valleys, sometimes at high rates of speed. Mudflows are usually more destructive of lives and property than any other type of volcanic activity. They can flow for many miles from the source. The dips given above for the peaks that surround the Guffey center are all on slopes made up primarily of mudflows. The recent explosive activity at Mount St. Helens in Washington State and Mount Pinatubo in the Philippines are examples of this type of explosive volcano.

Oligocene Lakes

Prior to the growth of the volcanic pile, all drainage from South Park was to the south. As the volcanic pile grew and mud flows traveled in all directions the drainage was dammed and two large lakes formed. The lakebeds at Florissant are famous for insect and tree fossils. A larger and less known lake covered much of South Park and left lenses of limestone with interbedded volcanic material in the **Antero Formation**. The outcrops of this formation have a north south trend from near Fairplay through a narrow band immediately east of Antero Reservoir and extending south along west side of the Agate Creek drainage. The northern part of this trend is termed the High Creek syncline. The Antero syncline is located in the southern part of the trend east of Antero Reservoir and extends over eight miles south. Lakebeds are also preserved six miles northeast of Hartsel overlying Precambrian rocks of the Elhorn thrust sheet.

The Antero Formation is a 670 to 2,000-foot unit that has three members. The lowest member consists of thin limestone beds, tuff, sandstone, conglomerate and minor shale (Stark et al, 1949). The limestones include algal beds and reefs that developed in shallow water near the lakeshores. The limestones are rarely over 12 feet thick; the tuff beds may be 100 feet thick. The middle member is fine-grained tuff, shale beds, and limestone lenses that are up to 20 feet thick. The topmost member is a poorly consolidated conglomerate with sandy interbeds. Vertebrate fossils (Mammalia teeth, jaw parts and bones), gastropods, wood, and algal reefs can be found in the formation (Stark et al, 1949, p.66).

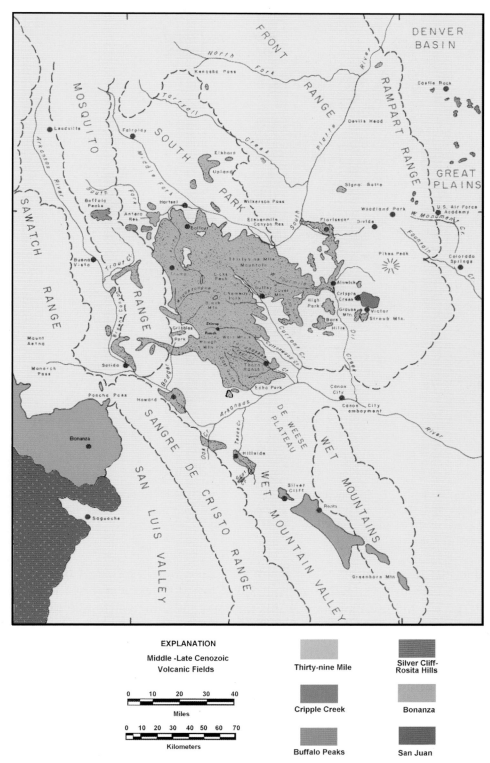

Geologic History Figure 11. Location of the Thirtynine Mile volcanic field in relation to other middle to late Cenozoic volcanic areas (from Epis, et al, 1980).

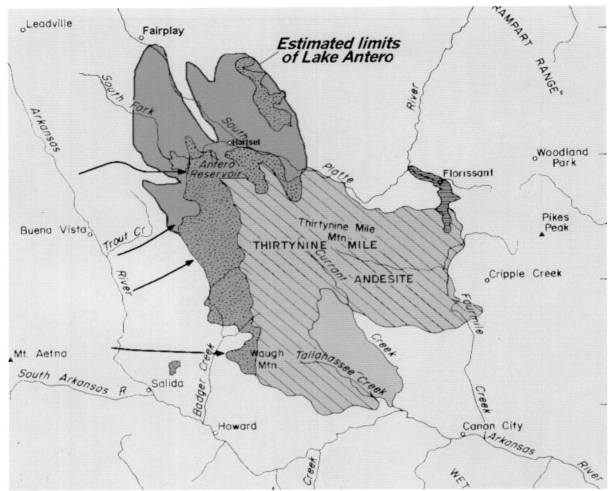

Geologic History Figure 12.   Present extent of the Thirtynine Mile Andesite showing how the Florissant (horizontal lines) and the Antero Formation (stippled) were deposited in water impounded by andesitic mudflows. Blue line shows the estimated extend of the Antero Lake over South Park. Arrows show trends of paleovalleys. (After Epis, et al, 1980).

It is probable that the elevation of the South Park lake was like that of the Florissant Lake, which has been variously estimated at from 3,000 to 8,000 feet above sea level (Chapin and Kelley, 1997). The highest mountain at this time would be the Guffey volcano, an estimated 7,000 to 8,000-foot height above the lake. The rest of the area still retained the subdued relief of the late Eocene.

Miocene-Pliocene (Neogene) Events

The most significant event of this time was the broad (epeirogenic) uplift of the High Plains and much of the Southern Rocky Mountain area. A major north-south rift system developed from southern New Mexico to the Leadville area of Colorado. Rift valleys are broad down-dropped troughs formed by faulting on both sides. The Rio Grande River from the San Luis valley of southern Colorado to near El Paso, Texas flows down the rift. The Upper Arkansas

River from north of Leadville to Salida drains the northern continuation of the rift. This is a rift valley system comparable to the famous East African Rift.

Because of epeirogenic uplift South Park experienced dramatic change during the Neogene from the low relief terrains of late Eocene time to the high mountain conditions that prevail today. Included were (1) an increase in the elevation estimated by some to have been 5,000 to 7,000 feet, (2) rejuvenation of old faults and development of new faults, (3) extensive erosion, and (4) the cutting of a new drainage outlet (South Platte Canyon) across the Front Range. During the early part of the Miocene there was volcanic activity and associated mineralization in the Cripple Creek district.

The only sediments of this age in the South Park region are assigned to the **Wagontongue Formation**. This formation only occurs south of Antero Reservoir at the southern end of the park along the divide that separates the Agate Creek drainage from the headwaters of Badger and Wagontongue Creeks. Two small areas of bad lands have been eroded in outcrops in sections 29 and 30, T. 14 S., R. 75 W. The beds are poorly consolidated fluvial conglomerate, sandstone and sandy clay. The pebbles are mainly derived from lava. Thickness ranges from 110 to an estimated 500 feet. Fossil teeth and bone fragments plus silicified wood have been reported (Stark et al, 1949, p.69). One perfect jaw of a species of equid (horse) of upper Miocene or lower Pliocene age was collected.

The **South Platte River canyon** across the Front Range is one of many examples of superimposed streams throughout the Rockies. Superimposed streams cut through mountainous areas rather than taking an easier route around the mountains. They are believed to have developed when the mountains were buried by sediments and to have maintained their route as the sediments were removed by erosion. Royal Gorge is nearby example. Following the courses of the Green, Colorado, North Platte, Laramie and other Rocky Mountain rivers will identify many examples of rivers that take direct routes across uplifted areas. Most of the superimposed canyon cutting started during the Neogene. The drainage of South Park to the east can be explained by the damming of the earlier south drainage during the Oligocene. Just why the river cut a straight northeast trending canyon has not been explained. There is no obvious line of weakness.

Pleistocene

Following the Neogene activity there was a period of erosion and widespread development in South Park of a high level surface that is covered by a thin deposit of gravel. This is a fairly mature surface as limestone and dolomite pebbles are rare. Quartzite and fine-grained igneous pebbles are common. Granites and other course grained igneous rocks show signs of deep weathering. Stark etal (1949, page 72) describes this terrace surface around Como and correlates it to other parts of the region. He dated the **Como surface** as pre-Illinoian (Pleistocene).

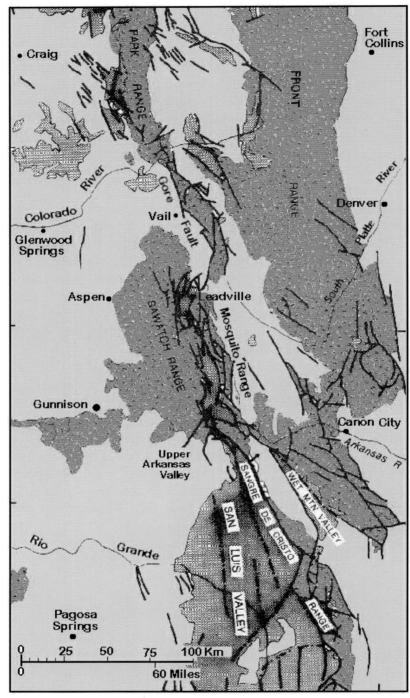

Geologic History Figure 13. Faults that were activated during the Miocene across the South Park region (Tweto, 1980). The amount of postvolcanic movement on the Current Creek Fault in the Thirtynine Mile Volcanic field is reported to be 300 meters (1,000 feet). The overall uplift of this area is estimated by some as 6,000 feet as recorded by the change in elevation of the Florissant lakebeds. In the Mosquito Range the uplift resulted in reactivation of the Mosquito and London faults and the modern mountains.

Geologic History Figure 14. Aerial view looking northwest across Buena Vista. This fault-bounded valley is near the north end of the Rio Grande Rift that extends from El Paso to past Leadville.

A gravel deposit of pre-glacial age perched near the crest of Pennsylvania Mountain is the source of a prolific gold placer. The gravels lie on an eroded Leadville Limestone surface in a position east of, and apparently downhill (at the time) from, the lode gold of London Mountain. A large nugget from this placer is on view at the Denver Museum of Natural History. This is the only placer working known to be in pre-glacial sediments.

The cyclical cooling of climate during the Pleistocene caused a series of glacial events. Only the younger events can be documented as younger glaciers usually occupy the same mountain areas and valleys as earlier and thus erase evidence of older occupation. After erosion that resulted from Neogene uplift, glacial erosion was the chief sculptor of the high mountains. An elevation of over 11,200 feet was necessary for the development of glaciers in the mountains around South Park (Meierding and Birgeland, 1980). Glaciers originate mainly on east slopes and in sheltered areas and only rarely on west facing slopes. The warmer afternoon sun normally will not allow the accumulation of enough snow on west-facing slopes.

Downstream from terminal moraines a long, broad area of **outwash stream deposits** is present. The most obvious is the broad valley that extends from Fairplay to two miles west of Hartsel. The sediments grade from very course cobble conglomerate near Fairplay in the area reworked by the gold dredge to a pebbly conglomerate in the south part. Gold settles out with the course material and peters out within three miles of the terminal moraine (end of placer mining). For a description of outwash and terrace deposits of Fourmile Creek and Jefferson Creek please see G. D. Singewald, 1950, plate 10.

Two periods of glaciation are easily recognized around Fairplay because the earlier was slightly more extensive. As the valleys had not been scoured to as great a depth by earlier glaciers as by the last, the earlier glacier was thinner, broader and longer. Large boulders in Fairplay Park in the east part of town are part of the **terminal moraine** of the earlier glaciation called **Illinoian (or Bull Lake stage**, depending on the author). Note the more rounded and weathered character of this moraine. The **terminal moraine** of the later glaciation (**Wisconsin or Pinedale stage**) is located immediately north of town where the South Platte River has cut a small canyon. Older glacial deposits are recognized in six valleys in the northwest part of South Park, namely Twelvemile, Fourmile, Platte River, Michigan and Jefferson Creeks and Tarryall Gulch. Terrace gravels correlative with these older glaciers are recognized downstream throughout South Park (Stark, 1949, plate 2, Singewald, 1950, plate 10).

Glaciation was a major sculpturing phenomenon for the valleys affected. Each of the glaciated valleys has been eroded to a characteristic U-shape. Terminal moraines are the most prominent feature, but each valley has a series of **recessional or substage terminal moraines** that can be correlated from valley to valley (Singewald, 1950, Plate 9). These substage terminal moraines are the result of melting back and subsequent re-advances of the glaciers, but each resurgence did not get as far down the valley as earlier stages. Thus we have the **Bristle substage** with placer workings at the Snowstorm mine (Sec. 19, T.9 S., R. 77 W.), and the **Alma substage** with placer workings at Alma. The placer mines of each substage are on the east side of the Middle Fork of the South Platte valley. The source of the gold is the lode gold deposits of the south flank of North Star Mountain west of Hoosier Pass (Singewald, 1950, plate 8).

Along the sides of the valleys are thick **lateral moraine** deposits and at the head of the valleys are beautiful **cirque** amphitheaters, usually with a lake in the bottom (Horseshoe Mountain cirque, Kite Lake, Emma Lake, Wheeler Lakes, etc.). Often large blocks of ice are incorporated in lateral and terminal moraines. When the ice melts, a small or large depression results that is called a **kettle**. Kettles are the source of clouds of mosquitoes. Commercial deposits of **peat** have been removed from filled-in kettles or lakes between lateral moraines. The largest of these in section 26, T. 9 S., R. 78 W. (along Lakeside Drive) was a lake dammed where lateral moraines of the Mosquito and Sacramento glaciers converged.

So we end in the present day enjoying the results of repeated and highly varying types of mountain building around a high altitude basin. The entire South Park area presently is being vigorously attacked by erosion. Study of the sand and mud load carried by any stream during spring runoff will show the erosive power of South Park streams.

Another sign of vigorous erosion, **rock glaciers**, are found in many valleys above timberline. A beautiful rock glacier can be viewed from Colorado Highway 9 flowing down a U-shaped valley high on the northeast flank of Mt. Lincoln (Colorado Highway 9 Road Log, Figure 7).

Economic Geology

Gold and Silver

These two metals are deposited in association with Late Cretaceous and Tertiary intrusives. The major producing areas are in the northwest part of Park County with a very minor amount of gold found in the Guffey area. There are three excellent US Geological Survey publications by Quentin D. Singewald that describe the gold and silver lode deposits of the London Mountain-Alma districts (1941) and the Beaver-Tarryall district (1942). A 1950 publication describes the history and role of glaciation in the deposition of placer gold downstream from the bedrock sources.

Gold was first discovered in 1859 in glacial deposits along Tarryall Creek north of Como. Placer gold was obtained from terminal moraines of glaciers that head in Montgomery Gulch and from outwash from the front of the glaciers. (See Boreas Road Log Figure 4.) From 1859 to 1937, the aggregate production was estimated at $1,250,000.

Lode gold of the Beaver-Tarryall District is found in a zone of intense contact metamorphism of east-dipping Maroon sediments around the Montgomery Stock. This small stock centers in the valley immediately north of Mount Silverheels. The ore deposits consist of "(1) veins and veinlets along fissures, (2) replacement bodies in metamorphosed limestone and (3) countless veinlets in extensively fractured porphyry and other brittle rock" (Singewald, 1942). There are no data on the amount of lode gold produced in this district. Please see Figure 285-10 and the discussion at Boreas MP 9.3 for additional information on the Beaver-Tarryall District.

Figure C9-4 shows the extent of late Wisconsin glaciation in the vicinity of Fairplay. The earlier Illinoisan glacial advance(s) extended at least a mile farther south than the terminal moraine of the Wisconsin glacier (Singewald, 1950, plate 10). Deposits of the earlier moraine underlie Fairplay and also can be found in a hummocky terrain west of the river. Placer gold has been obtained from each of the terminal and substage terminal moraines and from the outwash gravels south of the terminal moraines. Placer gold was also worked along Beaver Creek northeast of Fairplay. Figure C9-6 shows that at one or more times the glaciers rode over Beaver Ridge and terminated on the west side of Beaver Creek valley. A trip through the Fairplay area will show that all of the placer workings are either at the front or along the east side of the glacial moraines. This suggests that the source of placer gold was in the headwater area of the Middle Fork of the South Platte River. Up to 1950, the placers had yielded $4,000,000 in gold. Some placers, such as the Snowstorm property (Road Log C 9 MP 69.5), have been worked periodically up to 1999 depending on the price of gold.

A unique placer can be seen from Colorado Highway 9 and Mosquito Gulch road. There is a scarred area high on the north side of the sloping crest of Pennsylvania Mountain. It is above timberline at an elevation of approximately 12,250 feet. The mine is famous for large nuggets. One is reported to weigh 11.12 ounces and measure 3 by 2 ½ inches. This nugget is now in the Denver Natural History Museum. The parent gravels are preglacial and lie on top of eroded Paleozoic rocks. The nuggets show very little rounding and probably came from the London Mountain area, which was uphill and upstream at the time of deposition.

Singewald (1941) states that most of the important mines of the London Mountain-Alma District are within a few hundred feet of the London Fault on the footwall side, or within 4,000 feet of the Cooper Gulch fault on the hanging walls side (Economic Geology Figure 1). The productive areas are bunched near local centers of mineralization. "The principle types of ores are (1) gold-bearing quartz-sulphide veins of the London type, in or very close to the base of the Weber Formation, (2) silver-lead deposits in limestones, and (3) gold deposits in the quartzites of the Sawatch Formation…Gold deposits of each type are flanked by small silver-lead deposits, but the large silver-lead deposits are grouped near an independent local center of mineralization." The silver deposits of the Alma district are classified with the distant facies of ore. "The age relations with respect to the … intrusives and the faults suggest only one period of deposition. The ores formed from hydrothermal solutions exuded at depth from the same magma reservoir that earlier supplied the porphyries." Please see additional discussion, maps, and figures relating to ore deposition in the Mosquito and Buckskin Road Logs.

Rhodochrosite and Associated Crystals

Buckskin Road Log Figure 5 at MP 4.0 of the Buckskin Road Log shows miners at the portal of the only active mine in the South Park region. This is an 1870's silver mine that was reopened because of the report of large rhodochrosite crystals in the original tailings. The first exhibit at the Coors Mineral Hall of the Denver Museum of Natural History is a four-inch, deep red, rhodochrosite crystal. Then turning right you will enter a reproduction of the Sweet Home mine. Mind your head! In the walls with backlighting are reproductions of the spectacular crystal-lined pockets that are the objects of current mining. Gem collectors and museums around the world are being supplied with specimens like that in Economic Geology Figure 4 at a very profitable price for the operators of the mine. Concentrated exploration for these gems has been continuous since 1990.

A beautifully illustrated publication in the Mineral Record entitled *The Sweet Home Mine* by Moore and others (1998) covers the history of the mine and the Alma District. It contains a log of operations from 1990 to 1997 and describes the geology. The quality of the pictures of the various specimens and associated crystals will make the book a worthwhile possession.

In summary, the mineral-lined pockets occur in the hydrothermally altered zone in Precambrian metamorphic rocks around the Buckskin Stock. The age of crystal formation (30.6 to 27.6 my) appears to be much later than the age of the stock (70 my.?) and is possibly caused by late stage emanations off the magma that fed the Climax Stock (about 30 my.)

Uranium

There are three reported occurrences of uranium in South Park in friable, highly tuffaceous lakebeds of the Oligocene Antero Formation west of Hartsel (Malan, 1969). Minor production is credited to one of these occurrences where autunite, the predominant uranium mineral, is concentrated in thin, carbonaceous laminations along bedding planes. There has been deeper exploration southwest of Hartsel for late Eocene fluvial sediments in old valleys during the 1960's, but no report of findings.

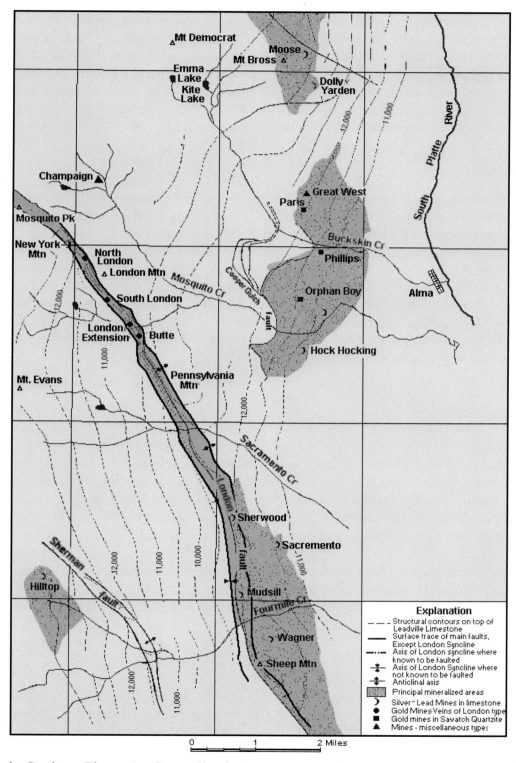

Economic Geology Figure 1. Generalized structure map of area near the London fault, showing relation of ore deposits to major structure (from Singewald, 1941).

Along Tallahassee Creek south of South Park in the southern part of the Thirtynine Mile Volcanic Field, 15 deposits ranging up to 25,000 tons in size have been exploited. There and in nearby drainages uranium ores have been found in pre-volcanic, arkose-filled, north-south valleys cut into the Late Eocene surface. Ore bodies one to ten feet thick are tabular, lenticular, and concordant to bedding. Uraninite is the predominant ore mineral. Nearly all the ore is associated with carbonaceous material in the fluvial host rocks. The uranium is leached from overlying volcanic deposits, transported by ground water, and precipitated where carbonaceous material (mainly fossil wood) provides a favorable reducing environment.

Coal

Three beds of bituminous coal are present in the basal part of the Laramie Formation north and southeast of Como (Washburne, 1910). Between 1875 and 1893, the King mines were worked on a large scale by the Union Pacific Coal Company, but were abandoned after the best and most easily available coal had been mined. The lowest coal occurs immediately above the basal sandstone and was reported to be the best commercial coal. It is from seven to ten feet thick, averaging about eight feet at the King and Wagon mines (three miles southeast of Como in Section 11, T9S, R76W.) The second seam (1 ½ to 4 feet thick) is 187 feet above the first and mined in a few places. The third seam (four feet thick) is 220 feet above the middle coal. Several mines were opened along the third seam near Como. Because of steep dip and limited thickness, these coal deposits are only of historic interest.

Peat

Commercial quantities of peat have been obtained from lakes and ponds between Mosquito and Sacramento Creeks. Some ponds had an origin as large kettles in the lateral moraines of Wisconsin glaciers. Large blocks of ice were often incorporated into the moraine deposits. After melting, the depression results in a feature called a kettle. Many of these mosquito-generators can be seen on a drive through this area. The ponds become filled with vegetation that eventually becomes peat. Mine the peat and the process is repeated.

A unique and large peat deposit was mined from a filled-in lake dammed by the confluence of the lateral moraines from the Mosquito and Sacramento Creek glaciers (Sections 25 and 26, T9S, R78W). Removal of the peat has rejuvenated the lake, which is a preferred place to watch duck families and elk late on a summer afternoon.

Gravel

Where there are glaciers, there is an ample supply of gravel. Moraines worked for deposits of gold yield gravel as a by-product. South of the terminal moraines cleaner glacial outwash gravels extend to Hartsel. Along Colorado Highway 9 north and south of Fairplay there are a number of commercial gravel quarries. Most are also placer mines when the price of gold is above $350/ounce. Currently the sale of gravel generates much more income than was ever obtained from gold.

Economic Geology Figure 2. Aerial view of London Fault from southeast.

Economic Geology Figure 3. Aerial view looking west at lakes rejuvenated by mining of peat. Large lake in upper left was formed by convergence of lateral moraines from Sacramento and Mosquito Creek glaciers. The other lakes are kettles in lateral moraines of Mosquito Creek glaciers.

Economic Geology Figure 4. The "Alma Queen" rhodochrosite from Houston Museum of Natural History collection. The main crystal measures 10.0 cm. The needle-like crystals are quartz. Specimen is from the Sweet Home Mine. From Moore, et al, 1998. Photograph by Wendell E. Wilson. Reproduced by courtesy of Mineral Record and photographer.

US Highway 24 Road Log
Buena Vista to Florissant

Parts of this road log are modified from a road log by Calkin, et al, 1972.

U.S. 24
Mileage
Markers

212.9   Junction of US Highway 24 and US Highway 285. From this point eastward the highway crosses the Upper Arkansas valley and follows the valley of Trout Creek up the western slope of the Mosquito Range to Trout Creek Pass.

213.3   **Colorado State Reformatory** to left is located on the flood plain of the Arkansas River. **Entering Johnson Village.** Along the west side of the valley are **three prominent terraces** that are Wisconsin, Illinoian, and pre-glacial in ascending order.

213.6   **Arkansas River.**

213.8   View to right (south) is along axis of widening segment of the **Upper Arkansas graben.** This graben is a north continuation of the **Rio Grande Rift** that extends from south of El Paso, Texas to north of Leadville.

Remnants of several **east-flowing paleodrainages** incised during the development of the **Late Eocene erosion surface** on the east flank of the **Sawatch anticlinal uplift** and filled with volcanic rocks of early Oligocene age are preserved along the east side of the upper Arkansas valley between Salida and Buena Vista. The paleovalleys trend at right angles to present major structural and topographic features. Reconstruction of Late Eocene drainage patterns indicate that pre-volcanic drainage was to the east. North-trending post-volcanic (post-Oligocene) faults on either side of the upper Arkansas valley have lowered and tilted the volcanic and Precambrian rocks, reversing original drainage and producing as much as 2,200 feet of structural relief between ash-flow tuffs at river level and the same tuffs along the southern Mosquito range to the east.

At 1:00 is the **Trout Creek paleovalley** that was aligned parallel to the base of the large ridge on the right (Triad Ridge). Late Eocene-early Oligocene streams flowed east through this paleovalley, which funneled ash-flow tuffs from **volcanoes in the Sawatch Range** into South Park and beyond. The flow of the Trout Creek valley was reversed by development of the Upper Arkansas valley rift during the Miocene and Pliocene.

214.8   Turnoff left to **BLM scenic overlook**. **Triad Ridge** at 2:00 (south of Overlook) has over 1,000 feet of the Wall Mountain Tuff exposed on the north side. This 36 m.y. old rhyolitic tuff probably erupted from a volcano located near the present Mount Aetna.

215.0   Strongly foliated **biotite-feldspar gneiss** in road cut. Similar lithology continues for next 1.5 miles, intruded locally by granite and pegmatite. Granites are assigned to the **1,700 m. y. age Denny Creek Batholith** (Geologic Map of Colorado), thus the sediments that have been metamorphosed to gneiss must be older than 1,700 m. y. The highway lies along the exhumed base of the north side of the Trout Creek pre-volcanic (Late Eocene) paleovalley as described above. The paleovalley extends northeastward for 10.5 miles through the crest of the Mosquito Range into South Park. It is filled with about 1,000 feet of layered volcanic rocks and associated gravels including the Wall Mountain Tuff at the base of the fill. (Please see DeVoto, 1971, Plate 1, Cross section C-C'.)

216.5   Gradational contact of Precambrian biotite-feldspar gneiss with biotite quartz monzonite that suggests igneous rock originated by melting of the metamorphic rocks (the ultimate phase of metamorphism in the rock cycle). View to right (south) shows crude bedding of Oligocene volcanic rocks filling the Trout Creek paleovalley.

217.7   Contact of Precambrian biotite quartz monzonite with biotite-microcline quartz monzonite augen gneiss. Cliffs on skyline between 1:00 and 2:00 consist of **Lower Paleozoic rocks** dipping northeastward away on the east flank of the Sawatch Range anticline.

220.5   **The Castles** are east west trending wall-like ridges immediately south of Trout Creek at 3:00 to 4:00. They consist of densely welded deposits of the **Wall Mountain Tuff.** Note the strong columnar jointing that typically develops when very hot welded tuffs or lavas slowly cool. The paleovalley extends straight ahead (northeast) up modern Mushroom Gulch through a notch in the crest of the Mosquito Range, whereas the highway turns north following Trout Creek. The Wall Mountain Tuff in this locality consists of multiple flows.

The Early Oligocene **Wall Mountain Tuff** exhibits maximum thickness and number of units in the paleovalleys (Epis and Chapin, 1974). No major **ash-flow eruptive centers** have been identified in the Thirtynine Mile field to the east. These facts, when considered with the eastward-flowing paleodrainages cited above, indicate that the ash flows were erupted from west of the Salida-Buena Vista area prior to formation of the upper Arkansas valley. The very widespread Wall Mountain Tuff will show up in many outcrops along US Highway 24 and has been traced over 100 miles downwind into the high plains area around Castle Rock, Colorado.

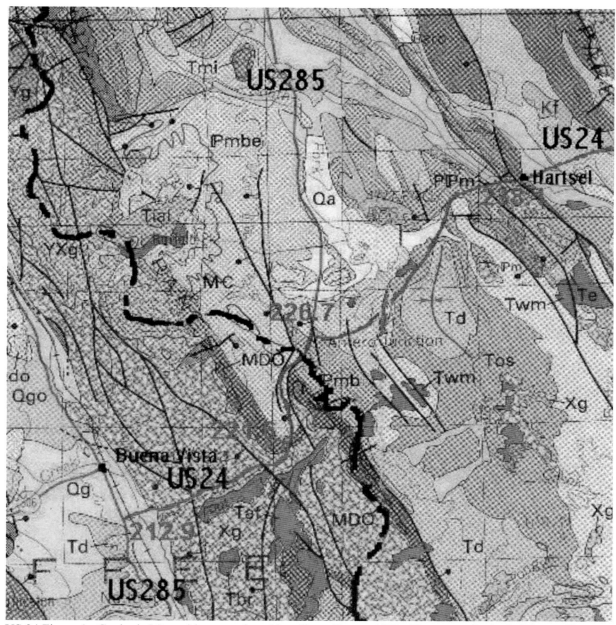

US 24 Figure 1. Geologic Map with route of road log. From Tweto, 1979. Please see Geologic History Figure 1 for an explanation of symbols.

221.6 **Precambrian-Ordovician angular unconformity and lower Paleozoic stratigraphy at Trout Creek**. The lower Paleozoic formations are fairly well exposed. The **Precambrian-Manitou unconformity contact** is clear-cut on the west side of the road. Note the chert in the lower part of the Manitou that is characteristic of many sections in central Colorado. Near the top of the Manitou there is evidence of pre-Harding erosion that formed caverns and sinkholes. The spring in the creek bottom appears to line up with the Manitou-Harding contact. Better exposures of the

Devonian and Mississippian formations can be found along the ridge northwest of Trout Creek.

US 24 Figure 2. On Trout Creek south of MP 220.5. View of Castles along Trout Creek Valley. The buttes are near vertical outcrops of Wall Mountain Tuff. See discussion and pictures at CR 187, MP 12.4 on the CR 53-CR 187 Road Log for additional discussion of these geologic wonders.

223.5   Highway follows general strike of Paleozoic formations and parallels a major fault zone that is the south continuation of the **Mosquito-Weston fault. High cliffs to right are lower Paleozoic formations dipping eastward** at 15-20 degrees. Highway is in the down-dropped block of Pennsylvanian Belden and Maroon Formations. High Peaks at 10:30 are the **Buffalo Peaks.**

225.5   **Trout Creek Pass** (elevation 9,346 feet). **Entering South Park** and Park County. Black shales, siltstones, graywackes and limestones of the **Belden Formation** are exposed in road cuts. R. H. DeVoto (1971, p. 68-69) reports that at this point we are just east of the center of a **deep Pennsylvanian-Permian trough (Colorado Trough)** that developed between the mountainous **Ancestral Front Range** to the east and **Uncompahgria** to the west. DeVoto describes the lower part of the black shale section as fresh water deposits and the overlying majority as being of marine origin. The Belden section is 1,630 feet thick at Trout Creek and thins to the east by onlap and facies change to Maroon red fluvial sediments. These relationships are confusing because of the abrupt lateral change from marine to nonmarine deposition along the east side of the trough. Study of DeVoto's explanation is recommended.

225.8   **Belden Formation** on left.

226.0   Highway descends east side of Trout Creek Pass to Antero Junction and **enters South Park**. The next 4.5 miles are in poorly exposed Pennsylvanian and Permian Maroon Formation that is folded and faulted along north trending structures.

226.7   **Antero Junction**. Continue to right (east) on US Highway 24. Junction is on **Maroon Formation** on east flank of **Kaufman Ridge uplift**, a south continuation of the **Mosquito Range**. **Kaufman Ridge** to southeast is steeply northeast **dipping Lower Paleozoic section**. (See DeVoto, 1971 for detailed description of this area.)

227.0   **North and South Hall Buttes** at 10:00. (See US Highway 285 Road Log).

228.2   **Antero Junction Anticline**, lower member of **Maroon Formation** is exposed.

US 24 Figure 3. At MP 230.1. East-dipping (30 degrees) outcrops of Wall Mountain Tuff on west flank of Antero Syncline.

230.1   **West edge of Antero Syncline**. Outcrops of **Wall Mountain Tuff** unconformably overlie the Maroon Formation. Dip is about 20 degrees east into a large, north-trending **Tertiary basin called the Antero syncline**. The basin is filled with over 3,000 feet of layered volcanic rocks, lake deposits and stream-laid clastic deposits. In ascending order, they include **Wall Mountain Tuff, Thirtynine Mile andesite, lower volcanic conglomerate, Antero Formation, Ash Flow 7 (all Oligocene) and the Trump and Wagontongue Formations (Miocene).** For next 5.5 miles the highway follows the northwestern flank of the Antero syncline. DeVoto (1971) believes the syncline is underlain by a thick section of Maroon Formation. If this section contains gypsum and salt beds like those at the saltworks north of Antero Junction, then the deep syncline may be a sag type of basin that developed as the underlying salt and gypsum were dissolved.

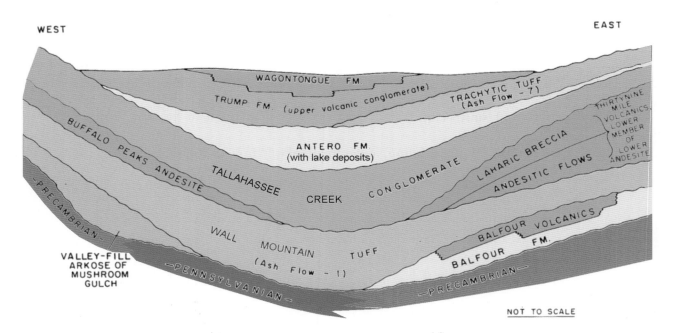

WEST   EAST

US 24 Figure 4. Cross-section of Antero Syncline. After DeVoto, 1971

230.2 **Limestone beds in Antero Formation**. These are approximately contemporaneous with the lake sediments at Florissant. Axis of the syncline is one mile southeast.

232.4 Hills at 11:00 are northwest dipping (32-34 degrees) **Wall Mountain Tuff**.

231.4 Hill at 9:00 is **Wall Mountain Tuff.**

234.1 Road to left to **Antero Reservoir**.

235.0 East Entrance to **Antero Reservoir**.

235.3 On left is the **South Fork of South Platte River.**

235.9 Red beds of **Maroon Formation east of Antero syncline**. There is a large remnant of **Wall Mountain Tuff** to the right.

238.1 **Junction US Highway 24 and Colorado Highway 9**. Massive sandstones of the **Garo Formation** (Jurassic?) are exposed in the road cut to the right. River to the left is flowing over **Morrison Formation** (Jurassic). The **Dakota Formation** (Cretaceous sandstones) forms cliff to left.

238.7 **South Fork of South Platte River.** South of the highway the South Fork leaves the Morrison, cuts a loop on **Precambrian rocks**, and reappears downstream on Cretaceous sediments. The Maroon Formation is absent in this area.

238.9 **Hartsel.** **Garo Sandstone** lies unconformably **on Precambrian** rocks just south of the road. The wooded hills to south are **Precambrian "islands"** surrounded by Tertiary mudflow and lake deposits. What they represent is the **irregular western edge of the Ancestral Front Range** (Pennsylvanian-Permian in age, see Geologic History chapter). From near the middle of the Ancestral Rockies trough at Trout Creek Pass to this point over **12,000 feet of Paleozoic section is lost by a combination of erosion and on lap** onto the western edge of the Ancestral Front Range.

The Colorado Midland Railroad was built through Hartsel in the 1880's.

240.0 **Junction with Colorado Highway 9,** continue east on US Highway 24. The surface trace of the north-northwest trending **South Park reverse fault** is at about this point. For next 7.5 miles the highway is over poorly exposed Cretaceous **Pierre Shale**.

241.2 **Middle Fork of South Platte River.** At 3:00 are **Thirtynine Mile Mountain** and **Saddle Mountain**. These mountains are composed mainly of **mudflow deposits** from the **Guffey Volcano**. Low relief knobby hills between the mountains and this point are on mudflow deposits from this volcano.

241.4 Hill on right is capped by **mudflow breccia** from Oligocene Guffey volcano 16 miles south-southeast. Bedrock under flow is **Pierre Shale**.

242.3 **San Isabel Ridge** on left is the trough of a **north-plunging syncline**. Section includes **Pierre Shale**, overlain by **Fox Hills Sandstone**, which is in turn overlain unconformably by the **South Park Formation** of Paleocene-Eocene age. The syncline is a **Laramide feature**. To the west of this syncline there is an anticline as shown on Sawatzky, 1972, Cross section A-A'. Well control (Clement and Dolton, 1970, Cross Section A-A') shows complex structure at depth related to the South Park Fault. The anticline is not easily seen at the surface because of the poor exposures in the Pierre Shale.

243.1 Small hill at 2:00 is **Glentivar dome**. The resistant formation at the top is the **Dakota Sandstone**. A rim of **Niobrara Limestone** can be seen on the north, west, and south sides. Shell Oil Company drilled this feature in 1956 and encountered Precambrian igneous rock at 500 feet. The Morrison rests on the Precambrian here with no Paleozoic section present.

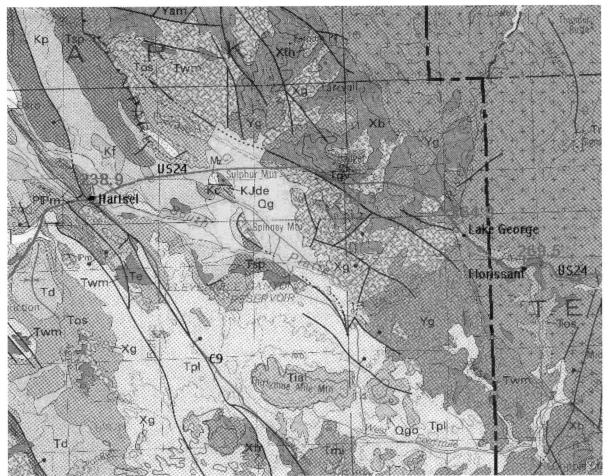

US 24 Figure 5. Geologic Map with route of road log. From Tweto, 1979. See Geologic History Figure 1 for explanation of symbols.

Maps and cross sections from a paper by D. L. Sawatzky, 1972 are included here to show the geology in three dimensions. North of the highway the basin deepens and is characterized by broad structures, primarily the Mexican Ridge Syncline. South of US Highway 24 the Cretaceous is progressive eroded so that the Thirtynine Mile volcanic pile sets on Precambrian rocks. The structure south of the highway is characterized by a series of faulted anticlines and domes.

Well and outcrop control confirm that there are no Paleozoic rocks in South Park east of Hartsel. Late Paleozoic erosion of the Ancestral Front Range removed all of the Paleozoic section in this area.

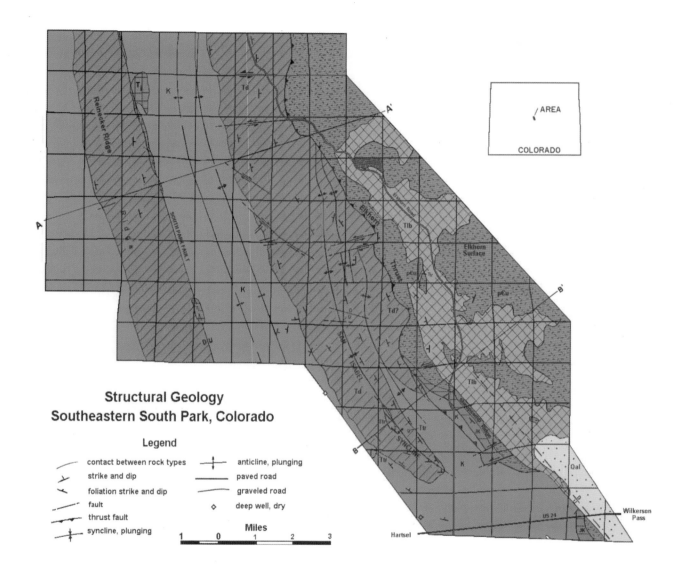

US 24 Figure 6. Geologic Map of area north of US Highway 24. Please note location of cross sections. From Sawatsky, 1972.

Shows of oil and gas were reported in tests drilled in the 1930, but no commercial discoveries of oil or gas have been made in South Park. Over 20 tests have been drilled since 1930, 14 of these on or near the Hartsel Anticline. Shell Oil Company carried out an integrated geologic-geophysical exploratory program in 1954-56. This program confirmed many of the structural complexities and reservoir potential, but failed to locate any accumulations. For a complete review of exploration to 1970, please see the Clement and Dolton paper. On the Elkhorn Road Log there is a discussion of unconfirmed rumors of a gas discovery drilled through the Elkhorn Thrust and into Cretaceous rocks of the Mexican Ridge Syncline.

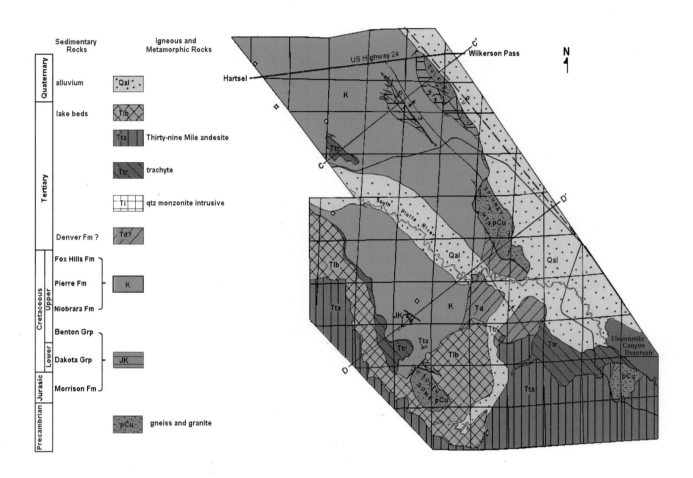

US 24 Figure 7. Geologic Map of area south of US Highway 24. From Sawatsky, 1972

The Elkhorn Thrust is prominent to the north and south, but not where US Highway 24 crosses it east of Sulfur Mountain. North of US Highway 24 the thrust sheet covers much of the east side of the Mexican Ridge syncline.

Structural Cross-sections
Southeastern South Park, Colorado

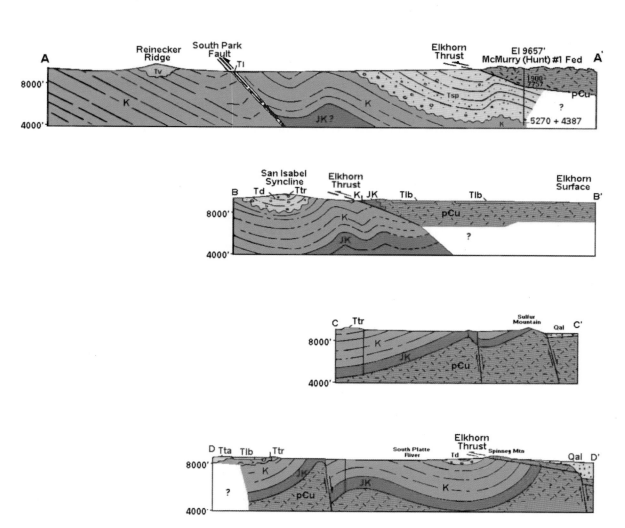

US 24 Figure 8. Cross-sections of the southeast part of South Park. Locations of sections are shown on US 24 Figures 6 and 7. After Sawatsky, 1972.

244.3 Low narrow ridge at 10:30 is **Sheepcamp Ridge**. It consists of **Precambrian rocks over lain by Morrison, Dakota and Pierre sediments**, all of which are **thrust westward** over the Pierre and Denver Formations along the **Elkhorn Thrust**. The thrust sheet continues north for at least 30 miles.

245.9 **Spinney Mountain** at 2:00 in middle distance the **Elkhorn thrust** trace curves around the west side of Spinney Mountain. **Precambrian rocks** have been **thrust westward over Cretaceous rocks**. South of Spinney Mountain Oligocene volcanic rocks from the Guffey volcano cover the overthrust.

246.4 **Sulphur Mountain** at 1:00. The ridge is formed by steeply west-dipping **Dakota Sandstone**. The relation of this feature with the Elkhorn thrust is uncertain.

247.2 Section in road cut is **Precambrian granite and metamorphic rocks** overlain by thin red and green **Morrison shales, Dakota Sandstone, Benton Shale and Niobrara Limestone**.

247.9 Road to left.

248.9 Road cut in **pediment gravels**.

249.8 **Glentivar**. CR 23 to right leads to Eleven Mile Reservoir. CR 23 to left leads to Tarryall Reservoir. The wooded hills straight ahead are the **Puma Hills**, composed of Precambrian igneous and metamorphic rocks. Between Sulphur Mountain and the Puma Hills the highway is on **pediment gravels covering Precambrian rocks** of the Elkhorn upland. This is a local portion of the **late Eocene, pre-volcanic erosion surface**. The Puma Hills are a **Neogene (Miocene-Pliocene) horst or tilted fault block** uplifted above the general level of the late Eocene surface. About 15 miles south are the high, heavily forested north slopes of **Thirtynine Mile Mountain**. This is part of the **north flank of the Guffey volcano**.

251.7 Hummocky **landslide terrain**.

254.3 **Wilkerson Pass** (elevation 9507 feet). **Leaving South Park**. Stop and review the Geologic Wonders of South Park that can be seen from the pass. **Precambrian rocks** here are mainly garnetiferous, biotite-quartz-plagioclase **gneiss**. **Pikes Peak** (14,109 feet) is on skyline to east. The **Late Eocene surface** is cut along the north shoulder of Pikes Peak, between it and Divide. The higher surface (about 12,500 feet) on south shoulder of Pike Peak is probably the same Late Eocene surface uplifted by Neogene faults.

254.5 Descending east side of Wilkerson Pass. View to south (west of Pikes Peak) is of the **Cripple Creek volcanic pile** resting on the **Late Eocene surface**. The Cripple Creek volcanism (Miocene) is younger than the volcanic pile of the Guffey area (Thirtynine Mile Volcanic Field).

Sharp knob at 2:00 is **Mt. Pisgah, a phonolite plug** in the western part of the Cripple Creek Field. Please read A. H. Koschmann (1949) for a description of the Cripple Creek gold field.

254.7 Copper mine on left. The highway follows a **fault** in Precambrian metamorphic rocks.

256.2 **Late Eocene surface** on **Rampart Range** straight ahead, underlain by **Pikes Peak Granite.** In foreground the same surface is cut in harder rocks as a **broad channel.** This surface extends northward into **Badger Flats** where it is covered by pre-volcanic conglomerate and the Wall Mountain Tuff. Neogene faulting has elevated the late Eocene surface on Rampart Range higher than Badger Flats.

257.4 South end of **Tarryall Range** at 10:00.

258.2 Junction with CR 31 to **Tarryall Recreation Area.** Muscovite-bearing **pegmatite** in road cut on left.

258.8 Fine-grained **quartz-monzonite** correlative with Precambrian **Boulder Creek Granite** (1700 m.y. group).

259.8 **Sillimanite gneiss.**

261.9 **Granite** in hill to left and in continuing outcrops.

263.1 Course-grained granite on right is correlative with Precambrian **Silver Plume Granite (1,400 m.y.)**

263.7 **Small mesa** at 9:00 is welded zone of **Wall Mountain Tuff** resting on **Precambrian granite.** Hills at 11:00 are southwestern part of quartz syenite-gabbro **Tarryall Lobe ring complex in the Pikes Peak Granite batholith** (US 24 Figure 9).

263.9 **Junction with CR 77** to Tarryall. **South Platte River** on left. Entering Oligocene **Florissant Lake Basin.**

264.6 Bridge across South Platte River. **Mesa** at 1:00 is capped by **Wall Mountain Tuff** resting on **Pikes Peak Granite (1 b.y.)** The tuff beds dip northeast beneath Florissant Lake Beds.

264.9 **Lake George.** For next 4.5 miles highway is in **northwest part of Florissant Lake Basin.** The first Colorado Midland passenger train from Colorado Springs reached the settlement of "Rocky" in 1887. George Frost constructed a dam at the mouth of Elevenmile Canyon (then Granite Canyon) and platted the nearby town of Lake George. For years ice was cut from the lake to refrigerate railroad boxcars.

266.0 Hills north and south of basin are **Pikes Peak Granite.** Southern rim of **syenite-gabbro ring complex** lies north on highway (See discussion of Precambrian rocks in Geologic History Chapter. There is a road log from Lake George to the center of the ring complex in Colorado School of Mines Studies in Colorado Field Geology No. 8, p. 27-29. Please see also a paper by R. A. Wobus, 1976 in that guidebook.). Small wooded knobs immediately south of highway are isolated outcrops of **Wall Mountain Tuff.**

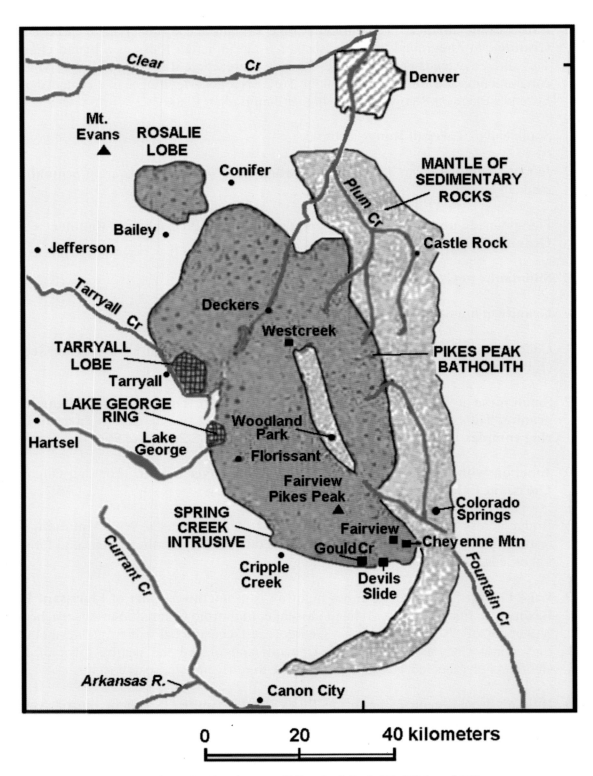

US 24 Figure 9. Sketch Map of Pikes Peak Batholith (Wobus, 1976).

266.6   **Florissant Lake Beds** on left are easily eroded and commonly covered by fan material from **grus** (deeply weathered zone) developed on Pike Peak granite.

266.9   Entering Teller County.

267.9   **Pre-volcanic conglomerate (Late Eocene)** resting on **Pikes Peak Granite** grus and capped by **Wall Mountain Tuff.** Note **lakebeds** near ranch on left. Sharp peak on left is **Crystal Peak**, source of amazonstone, topaz, smoky quartz, limonite after siderite, etc. in cavities in Pikes Peak Granite.

268.2   **Wall Mountain Tuff** on left. **Florissant Lake Beds** in road cut north of creek. All of the lakebed outcrops contain abundant leaf and twig fossils and an occasional bug or fish impression.

268.9   Note **Late Eocene surface** above Florissant.

269.5   **Florissant Lake Beds** on left and right of highway.

269.5   **Florissant. Wall Mountain Tuff** to left, north of Post Office. Junction with road to Florissant National Monument and Cripple Creek. See **Guffey-Florissant Road Log** for additional information on this area and a picture of the lakebeds.

End of road log.

US 24 Figure 10. Aerial view looking north at Hartsel.

US Highway 285 Road Log
Antero Junction to Pine Junction

US Highway
285 Mileage

161.8 **Antero Junction of US Highway 24 and US Highway 285**. Travel north on US Highway 285. There is a separate road log in this book for US Highway 24 from Buena Vista to Antero Junction and east to Florissant. Red sediments in road cuts are Maroon Formation.

162.1 – 162.8 **Thin bedded limestones** in low relief road cuts on both sides of the highway are flat lying and interbedded with ash beds and volcano-clastics. All appear to be water-lain and to be near the west edge of the Oligocene Lake Antero. Wood impressions can be found in some limestone beds.

164.2 **Saltworks** about one mile east. The saltworks was built in 1864 and operated in the early days of mining and homesteading of this area. It is at a spring where salty water issues from a gypsum-bearing section near the base of the Maroon Formation. The Maroon Formation of this area is described by R. H. DeVoto (1970) as 6,000 to 10,000 feet of gray, greenish-gray, red and yellowish-buff arkosic sandstones, conglomerates, siltstones and shales. Sequences of gypsum up to 50 feet thick occur in the lower part of the formation. Salt springs and sinkholes indicate that salt was deposited along with the gypsum.

US 285 Figure 1. Ruins of salt works at north base of East Hall Butte.

West Hall Butte and East Hall Butte to right. DeVoto reports that 500 feet of **Buffalo Peak Andesite** caps these buttes. Sanders, *et al*, 1976, report 565 feet of the same unit on top of 1,100 feet of tuffs and breccia of Oligocene age at **Buffalo Peaks** at 9:30. In all areas the section including the Buffalo Peak Andesite lies on eroded Wall Mountain Tuff. The Hall Buttes and Buffalo Peak deposits appear to be remnants of the filling of a deep valley in the Late Eocene surface. The andesite flow either came from a source at West Buffalo Peak or another source to the west. The relation whereby the Buffalo Peak deposit is 2,000+ feet higher than that of the Hall Buttes may be the result of reversal of throw on the Mosquito-Weston fault (along the east side of Buffalo Peaks) during Neogene uplift of the area. On the east side of East Buffalo Peak there is a step down terrace that resulted from Neogene faulting.

US 285 Figure 2. Looking north from Antero Junction at West and East Hall Buttes.

165.7 **Buffalo Creek**. Antero Reservoir on the South Fork of the Platte River is two miles east.

167.1 Steep dips in red beds of **Maroon Formation**. The underlying Maroon sediments are believed to include thick beds of salt. This complex structuring may be the result of upward movements of that salt.

167.6 **Buffalo Springs Camp Ground** road to left.

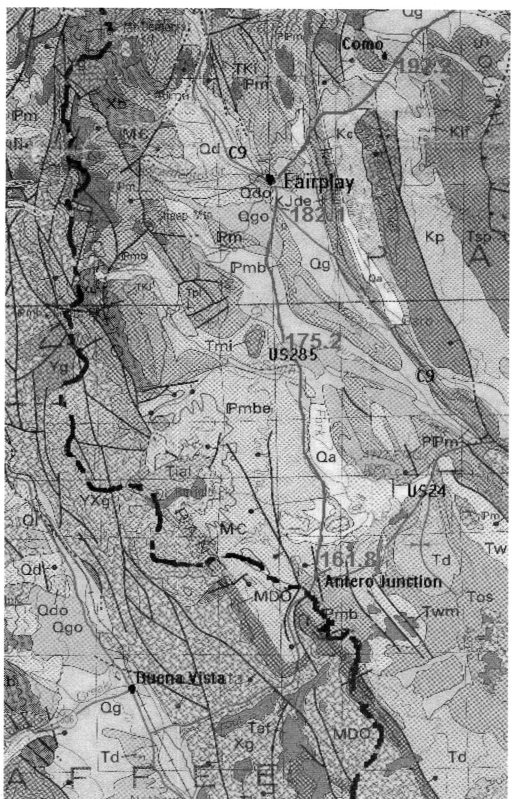

US 285 Figure 3. Geologic Map with route of road log (from Tweto, 1979). See Geologic History Figure 1 for an explanation of symbols.

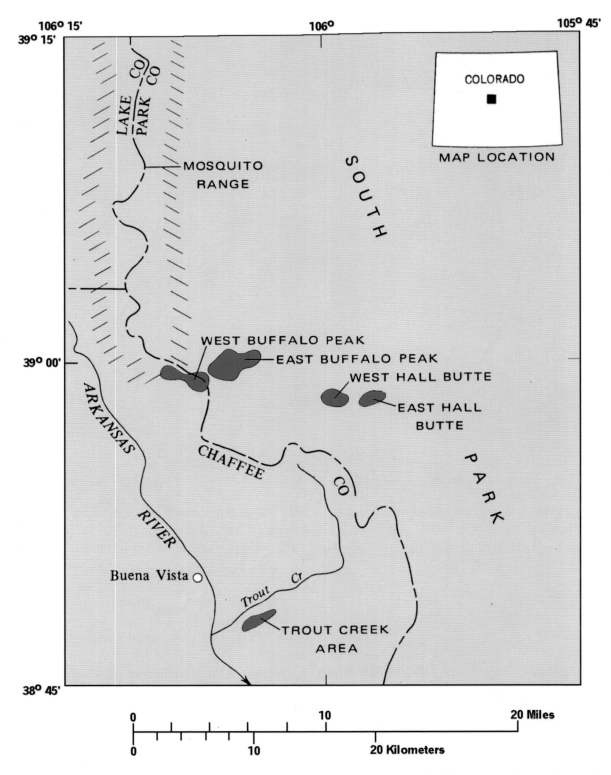

US 285 Figure 4. Location of Buffalo Peaks Andesite at Buffalo Peaks, Hall Buttes, and Trout Creek (from USGS Bulletin 1405f).

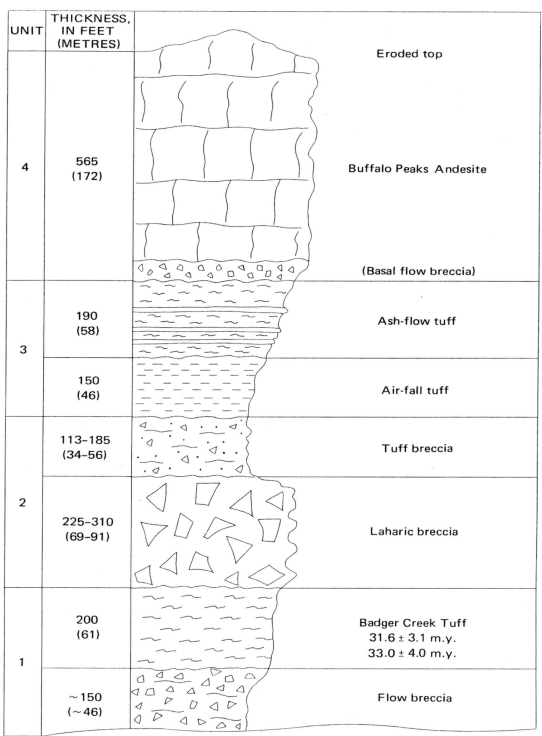

UNIT	THICKNESS, IN FEET (METRES)		
4	565 (172)		Eroded top
			Buffalo Peaks Andesite
			(Basal flow breccia)
3	190 (58)		Ash-flow tuff
	150 (46)		Air-fall tuff
2	113–185 (34–56)		Tuff breccia
	225–310 (69–91)		Laharic breccia
1	200 (61)		Badger Creek Tuff 31.6 ± 3.1 m.y. 33.0 ± 4.0 m.y.
	~150 (~46)		Flow breccia

Floor of early Oligocene paleovalley

US 285 Figure 5. Composite columnar section of volcanic rocks at Buffalo Peaks (from USGS Bulletin 1405f).

168.2 **Maroon redbeds** on left, note east dip. Maroon redbeds of Pennsylvanian age are the bedrock from Antero Junction to east of Fairplay. For most of this distance, they exhibit a consistent 20-degree east dip of the east flank of the Sawatch Anticline.

168.3 **Maroon redbeds with west dip**. Folding may be the result of salt flowage or solution of basal Maroon evaporites.

168.8 **Rhubarb patch** within road right of way on west side of road. Please be careful of high-speed traffic. Best to cut during June. My favorite is rhubarb custard pie. My address is 1657 Park County 1. Please keep this patch our secret!!

172.5 **CR 22 to Weston Pass** (11,900 feet) to left. This pass was an important stage and freight link to the Leadville Mining District prior to the building of the railroad to Leadville.

172.6 **South Fork of South Platte River**.

175.2 **Black Mountain** (10,568 feet) at 9:00. (Yes, there are two "Black Mountains" in Park County). Stark, *et al*, 1949, describes the igneous rocks in this mountain as intrusive quartz monzonite porphyries. Stark thought them to be related to the white and gray porphyries of the Leadville and London Mountain districts. Zortman, et al, 1995 report an age of 36 m.y., which would suggest a possible tie to the extrusive rocks at Buffalo Peaks.

There is an **anomalous boulder field** on the northeast flank. The boulders include very large (ten-foot diameter) granite and gneiss boulders that probably came from the Weston Pass area. They could have been carried by a glacier, but there is no known Pleistocene glaciation that extended into this area.

Ranchers report that there are several **sink holes** west of Black Mountain. These are probably the result of solution of Maroon salt deposits.

US 285 Figure 6. View of Black Mountain and Buffalo Peaks from north along US Highway 285

At 9:00, **High Creek Fen.** There is a small stand of blue spruce about three-quarters of a mile east of the highway. R. H. Mohlenbrook (1995) reports in *Natural History* that there is a sedge-covered fen here, created by the constant flow of ground water to the surface. There are more rare plant species in this fen than in any other wetland site in Colorado. The Nature Conservancy has acquired 500 acres of the wetlands and the area has been declared a Colorado Natural Area. The area is a remnant of glacial age flora. The nearest habitats of some of the plant species found here are in Alaska, Yukon and Yellowstone Park. This is also a great area for bird watching. The birds are here because of the bugs. Best to visit the fen on a cool or windy day. The deerflies are vicious on calm summer days. I have seen people run for their cars to escape the biting flies.

176.6 Road to right through fence gate to **parking area north of fen**. Note peat section partially removed south of parking area.

178.8 **CR 5** to left. This is another route to Weston Pass.

179.4 **CR 20** to left.

179.7 **Fourmile Creek**

181.0 **Sheep Mountain** at 9:00.

US 285 Figure 7. View to northwest across High Creek Fen (area of spruce trees in foreground). Buffalo Peaks in distance.

181.9 **Fourmile Creek road** to left. This road climbs to silver mines near the saddle between Horseshoe Mountain and Mount Sherman. Features to see along this road are **glacial deposits** typical of valley glaciers in this area, the **London Fault** just west of **Sheep Mountain,** and beautifully exposed faulted outcrops of Lower Paleozoic sediments and Late-Cretaceous-Early Tertiary sills in the spectacular **cirque carved into the east side of Horseshoe Mountain.**

182.1 **Junction Colorado Highway 9 South**. The **placer workings** southeast of Fairplay are described on the Highway 9 Road Log. The highway for next half mile is on the **outwash** of the Illinoian and Wisconsin terminal moraines of the Middle Fork of the South Platte River glacier.

182.5 Aspen and conifer covered ridges to left of highway are underlain by the **Illinoian Terminal Moraine**.

US 285 Figure 8. View from northwest across Fourmile Creek of Sheep Mountain. London fault passes through saddle on near side of Sheep Mountain.

US 285 Figure 9. At the headwaters of Fourmile Creek, this view is south across Horseshoe cirque. Faults (up to east, left) cut Paleozoic beds that are intruded by sills (the more massive beds in wall).

US 285 Figure 10. View north across Fairplay of Mount Silverheels (13,817 feet). Note steep east dip of ledges in the middle slopes. Singewald (1942) maps these as erosion-resistant igneous sills intruded between layers of the upper part of the Maroon Formation. Sills from the Montgomery Stock cap the mountain. The Tarryall-Beaver Creek gold district is in the contact metamorphic zone around the Montgomery Stock immediately north of Mount Silverheels. At Palmer Peak (12,526 feet) on the right sills have coalesced into a laccolithic body.

182.9 Middle Fork of South Platte River.

183.0 Junction Highway 9 North.

183.1 Illinoian Terminal Moraine one block north of highway (north of Fair Grounds.)

183.6 Beaver Creek

183.9 Road crosses outcrops of Maroon Formation. Dip is 20 to 30 degrees to east. The elongate ridge to the right on the skyline is **Red Hill Ridge** (Dakota Hogback on some maps), held up by the sandstones of the Garo-Morrison-Dakota sequence. The bald-topped hill at 11:00 is **Little Baldy Mountain.**

US 285 Figure 11. Aerial view looking south along Red Hill. The outcrop of east-dipping Dakota Sandstones causes this hogback. The lower band of pine trees on the west side marks the outcrop of the Garo Sandstone

185.2 **Crooked Creek**. Peat deposits in Quaternary alluvium to left of road at this bend. **Mount Silverheels** at 10:00. Just north of Mount Silverheels is the **Montgomery Stock,** the center of the **Tarryall Creek gold field**. For a very interesting description of this gold field please see Q. D. Singewald's 1942 USGS Bulletin 928-A on the Beaver-Tarryall Area.

186.2 Exposures of **Garo Sandstone** on right.

186.4 **Red Hill Gap**. Stop on right. Dip is 32 degrees to east. First sandstone at west side of gap is the **Garo Sandstone**, then a shallow valley on the **Morrison Formation** (note varicolored shales), then eastward the road descends diagonally across the **Dakota Sandstone**. Above the Dakota Sandstone in Trout Creek Valley the **Benton Shale, Niobrara Limestone** and **Pierre Shale** are exposed. (Yes, there are two Trout Creeks in this area.)

186.7 Descending hill, **Dakota Sandstone** on left.

186.9 Gray shale exposure at 12:00 is **Pierre Shale**. Hill is capped by Late Tertiary terrace gravel.

187.6 **Petrified Hereford** right of road at curve. The **Niobrara Limestone** is capped by a pine trees north of the highway.

US 285 Figure 12. At MP 186.4. Road cut through east-dipping Garo Sandstone at Red Hill Gap.

US 285 Figure 13. At MP 186.7. Road cuts in Dakota Sandstone. Note cross bedding and soft character. Isolated grove of trees on far right overlies outcrop of Niobrara Limestone.

US 285 Figure14. At MP 187. View to southeast of Reinecker Ridge. The ridge is composed of a series of mudflow deposits that filled a valley from north to south. Close look at the south-sloping bedding in the ridge shows the shingle-like succession of mudflow deposits. The source volcano may have been over the Montgomery Stock immediately north of Mount Silverheels. This author guesses the age of the volcano to be Oligocene. Others have assigned these extrusive rocks to the South Park Formation (Paleocene and Eocene).

187.9   Heavily forested ridge at 3:00 is called **Reinecker Ridge**, 10,363 feet (Basin Ridge on some maps). This ridge contains a **unique sequence of Tertiary extrusive igneous rocks**. It is in the middle of a syncline that is bound on the east by the South Park Fault. The igneous rocks are **ignimbrite flows overlain by 600+ feet of mudflow breccias (laharic breccias)**. The direction of deposition indicates that they came from a volcano to the north. Reinecker Ridge is 13 miles long and one to two miles wide. These extrusive flow deposits probably **filled a Late Eocene valley**. They are hard and resistant to erosion. The section on either side was Pierre Shale, which is easily eroded, **resulting in a topographic inversion whereby the earlier valley is now a mountain.**

189.2   **CR 7** to right. To view excellent exposures of the **mudflow deposits** turn left 0.7 miles down this road onto **Gap Road**. There is another left turn at 2.1 miles into a **box canyon**. The mudflows (US 285 Figure 12) are exposed in this canyon from 2.2 to 2.5 miles (Top of Reinecker Ridge). The very angular particles in the mudflows are pebble to boulder-size clasts of medium-grained, biotite-hornblende-feldspar igneous rocks that appear to be either ignimbrites or volcanic bombs.

189.3   Road cut on right in **ignimbrites** near base of Reinecker Ridge volcanic section.

189.0   At 9:30, **Little Baldy Mountain**. A very complexly faulted area of east-dipping Maroon through Dakota sediments that are intruded by many sills derived from the Boreas Stock.

189.6 Approximate position of **South Park fault**, a high-angle east-dipping reverse fault. Here the fault does not cut the Late Tertiary terrace. This fault continues north along the west side of the Boreas stock into the Blue River drainage area. The fault trends south along the east side of Reinecker Ridge, through the Hartsel area to connect with the Current Creek fault, and then farther south along the east side of the Wet Mountains, an **over 150-mile long fault**.

189.7 The **high level terraces** here have not been identified.

191.0 Outcrop of **Pierre Shale** to right.

US 285 Figure 15.   Outcrop of mud flow breccia in Gap Road canyon.

191.0 **Monzonite porphyry sill** intruded into Pierre Shale. There are many other such intrusives in this area. This one is dated at 42 m.y. (Zortman, 1995) and appears to be an intrusive from the Boreas Stock north of Como.

191.7 At 3:00, **Como Lake**. This looks like a **deflation feature** where wind has progressive removed dust from a **buffalo wallow**, gradually increasing the wallow in size during dry periods.

192.2 **Junction County Road 50 to Como and Boreas Pass**. Highway is on a Late Tertiary terrace.

192.5 Junction with Elkhorn Road. Please see the road log for this road.

US 285 Figure 16.   Sign on Reinecker Ridge road. Not all of the natives are friendly.

194.0   **Tarryall Creek.   Glacial outwash** material on either side of creek.   **Boreas Mountain** at 9:00 is near the center of the very large **Boreas Stock.**

194.4   **Fox Hills Sandstone and Laramie Formation** dipping east into syncline. Just east of the highway and about 4 miles south coal was mined from Laramie Formation beds during the late 1800's.

196.1   At 3:00. **High terraces** on either side of creek to southeast are remnants of **Late Eocene surface**.

Michigan Creek.   Michigan Hill at 10:00 is north end of the **Mexican Ridge syncline** that is 24 miles long and 5 to 6 miles wide. It is filled with up to **8,000 feet** of **Early Tertiary course debris (South Park Formation)** derived from the contemporaneously uplifted and intruded mountains on the west, north and east.

US 285 Figure 17. At MP 191.1. Igneous sill intruded between layers of Cretaceous marine shale. Dip is to the east at about 20 degrees.

Some of the fill is extrusive tuffs and andesite biotite-hornblende ignimbrites of Eocene age, probably from the **Boreas Stock**. South of the highway, the eastern part of the syncline is covered by the **Elkhorn Overthrust** where **Precambrian crystalline rocks** (granites of the 1,400 m.y. old Kenosha Batholith and metamorphic rocks) have been **thrust westward over the deepest part of the South Park Basin.** The approximate front of the overthrust block can be seen to the southeast as the west side of the hummocky, pine covered hills.

The city of Aurora tried to develop a rechargeable water resource from the center of the syncline by drilling wells into the water-bearing, coarse-grained fill (some wells were drilled through the overthrust) and withdrawing water at the same rate as it is recharged by Tarryall, Michigan, Jefferson, and other creeks crossing the outcrops of the South Park Formation. Their proposal was defeated in court.

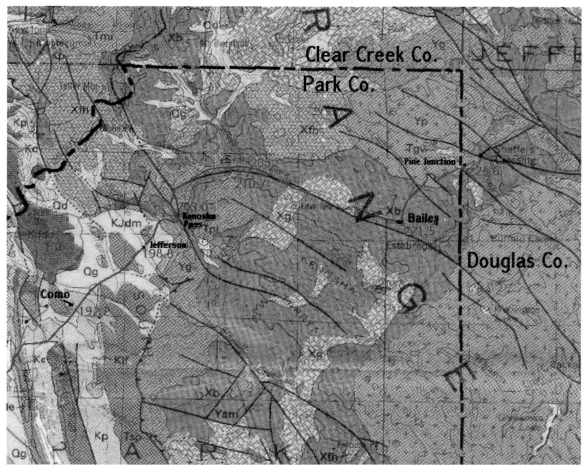

US 285 Figure 18. Geologic Map with route of road log (from Tweto, 1979). Please see Geologic History Figure 1 for an explanation of symbols

197.9 Crossing **outwash gravels** from glaciers that were near the headwaters of Michigan Creek.

198.8 **Jefferson**. There is a **Late Tertiary terrace** south of town on either side of Jefferson Creek.

199.3 At 9:00, **Jefferson Hill**, two and a half miles northwest, is an **intrusive plug** (small stock) dated at 56 m.y. (Paleocene), Zortman, 1995.

200.1 Crossing valley **eroded** into soft **Pierre Shale** section.

200.5 At 10:00, **Dakota Sandstone** outcrops in hill.

200.0 In road cuts on left, **steeply southwest dipping Cretaceous section** (mainly the Dakota Formation). The section here was **dragged upward** by **the uplift of the Front Range**.

202.2 Contact, **Dakota on Precambrian**.

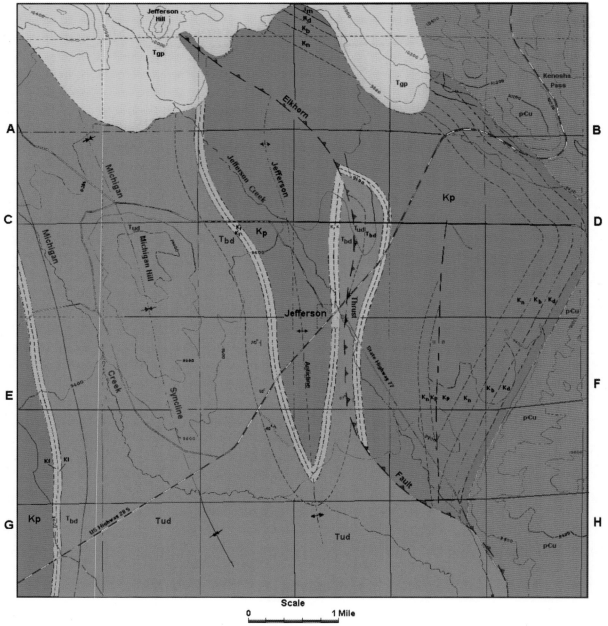

US 285 Figure 19. Geologic Map of the Jefferson are by N. K. Yacoub, 1965. This mapping is based on outcrops and a magnetic survey. The west-dipping Cretaceous and Tertiary rocks from just northeast of Jefferson to the Kenosha Pass are mapped as being above the Elkhorn Thrust. See US 285 Figure 20 for legend.

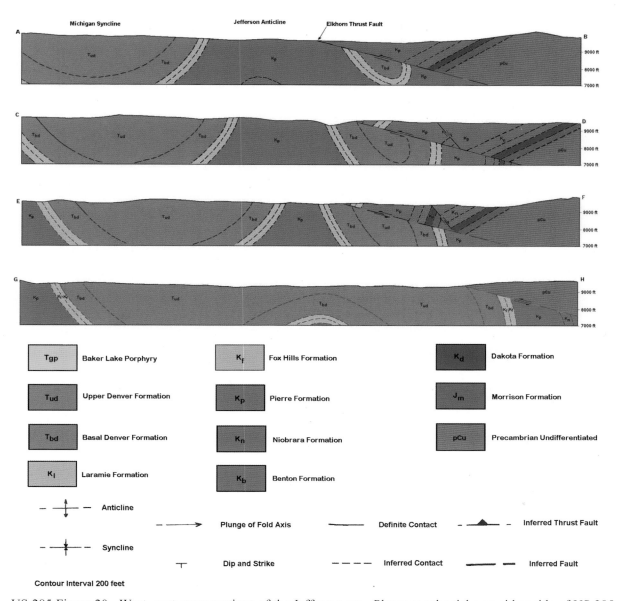

US 285 Figure 20. West- east cross-sections of the Jefferson are. Please see the ticks on either side of US 285 Figure 19 for location of the sections. From N.K. Yacoub, 1965

202.4 Scenic Overlook. An excellent opportunity to review features of the South Park region. In the foreground the trace of the **Elkhorn Thrust** curves to the south. The topography over the thrust is rolling hummocky hills with scattered pine cover. Northwest of the fault the **South Park Formation** is characterized by grass-covered lowlands. In the middle distance to the southwest is **Reinecker Ridge**, farther on is the **Mosquito Range and Buffalo Peaks**, and very far to the southwest peaks of the **Sawatch Range** can be seen.

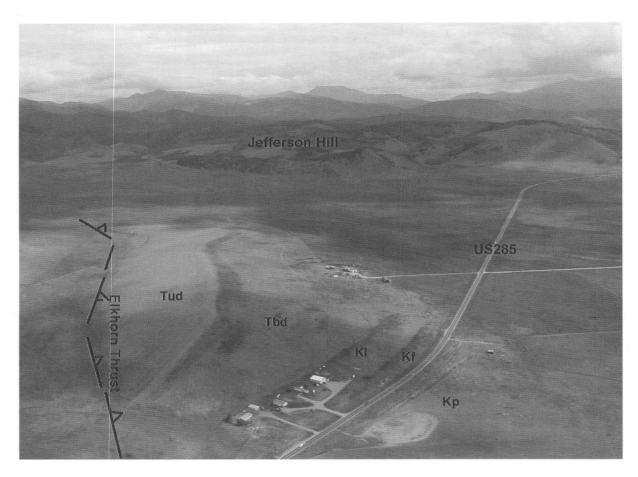

US 285 Figure 21. Aerial view looking north from above Jefferson. Please compare with the presentation on the geologic map, US 285 Figure 19 and Cross Section C-D on US 285 Figure 20.

203.0 Kenosha Pass. **Leaving South Park.** Crystalline rocks are **metasedimentary gneiss** of 1800+ m.y. age **intruded by granitic rocks** of the 1,400 m y. **Kenosha Batholith**. Mountains east of the pass exhibit the low relief of the **Late Eocene erosional surface.**

204.2-206.6 Granite.

207.3 Hoosier Creek and Junction **CR 60.**

207.5 Webster and North Fork of South Platte River. Highway from here to Bailey follows the North Fork of the South Platte River, which in turn is controlled by a zone of weakness along the **Shawnee Fault.** This is a curving northwest-southeast fault in the Precambrian that is upthrown on the north side (Kelley and Chapin, 1997). Webster was once a junction of toll roads leading northwest over Webster Pass to the Montezuma mining district. Kilns at Webster produced charcoal.

209.9 Roberts Tunnel Portal. Water from Lake Dillon on the west side of the Continental Divide is diverted to here for use as part of the Denver water supply.

210.7 **Grant** and junction **CR 62**, Guenella Pass road.

216.2 **Shawnee**. This was a stage stop on the Denver-Leadville Stage line during the 1860's. Note metamorphic **rocks** south of river (south of fault) and **granite** outcrops north of the river.

216.7 **Santa Maria Del Norte.** Established as a camp for underprivileged children in 1932. The "Christ of the Rockies" statute stands 33 feet high on a 22-foot pedestal.

220.4 **Glenisle Resort,** which was built in 1900. Now included in the National register of Historic Places. Metamorphic rocks are present on both sides of the river.

221.5 **Bailey**: road starts climb of long hill. In 1864, William L. Bailey settled in this area. In 1873, the Denver, South Park and Pacific Railroad was build through here to tap the seemingly inexhaustible supply of timber in the Platte Canyon area.

US 285 Figure 22. View across South Park from Kenosha Pass. Reinecker Ridge in the middle ground, Buffalo Peaks on left skyline and Mosquito Range on right skyline. In the far distance peaks of the Sawatch Range can be seen.

222.0-224.1 In road cuts **metamorphic shist**, **granite** and some crosscutting **dikes** of granitic rock are present.

224.4 Junction **CR 72**.

225.1 **Pikes Peak Granite (1,040 m.y.).** Contact with older Precambrian rocks at 12:00. This is the southern edge of the Rosalie Lobe of the Pikes Peak Granite Batholith. Please see US Highway 24 Road Log Figure 6.

225.6 **Typical weathered Pikes Peak Granite.** Weathering causes a breakdown of this granite to a **course gravel called "grus".**

225.6 **Pine Junction.** From here to **Turkey Canyon** the highway crosses the **north end of the Pikes Peak Batholith**. There are occasional inclusions (**xenoliths**) of metamorphic rocks. In Turkey Canyon watch for the east edge of the batholith and older metamorphic rocks before reaching the Red Rocks of the foothills. Note that the redbeds of the Red Rocks area are the same age as the Maroon Formation of South Park.

End of Road Log.

Colorado Highway 9 Road Log
U. S. Highway 50 to Hoosier Pass
Parts of this road log are taken from a Canon City to Breckenridge road log by
L. C. Gerhard, Ronald Chase and J. H. Lewis (1970)

Colorado 9
<u>Mileage</u>

0.0   Starting north from junction US Highway 50 and Colorado Highway 9.   The
       Morrison Formation is exposed along US Highway 50 by the OK Corral.

0.1   **Twelvemile Park** ahead is **floored by Cretaceous sediments**. The geologic map
       shows a **major fault** along the west side of the valley and Morrison on Precambrian
       rocks along the east side. No Paleozoic rocks are exposed in the valley.

       Section includes: **Cretaceous**
                                Niobrara Limestone
                                Carlile Shale
                                Greenhorn Limestone
                                Graneros Shale
                                Dakota Group
                                        Dakota Sandstone
                                        Purgatoire Formation
                        Jurassic
                                Morrison Formation
                        Precambrian rocks

0.3   The **Purgatoire Formation** is exposed on right in gulch.

0.4   **Graneros Shale** in road cut is poorly exposed.

0.5   **Morrison Formation** is exposed to right on flank of syncline and is **faulted against
       Precambrian rocks**.

0.6   **Dakota Group** is in the gulch on right. **Graneros Shale** is in road cuts.

0.8   **Upper Graneros and lower part of Greenhorn Limestone** are exposed in road cuts.

1.1   **Greenhorn Limestone** is exposed in road cut.

1.3   Roadcut on left is in the **Carlile Shale**. Greenhorn outcrops are in the knob to right.

C 9 Figure 1. Geologic Map with route of road log. From Tweto, 1979. Please see Geologic History Figure 1 for an explanation of symbols.

1.4   **Fluvial gravels**. High gravel here is considered equivalent to Nussbaum Alluvium of earliest Quaternary age.

1.8   **Pleistocene soil.**

2.5   **Dakota Group is** in the gulch on right.

2.8   Roadcut in **Carlile Shale**.   Cut is capped by **Niobrara Limestone**.

2.9   **Niobrara Limestone** on right.

3.1   **Upper part of Niobrara Limestone** on right.   Entire section is **infaulted into Precambrian rocks** that form low ridges.

3.2   Bridge

3.7   At 9:00, high pediment is capped by **Verdos Alluvium** containing **Pearlette Ash**. Sharp ridge at 3:00 is nearly vertical **Dakota Sandstone**.

4.4   **Carlile Shale** in cut to right.

5.1   **Tertiary alluvial gravels**.

5.7   **Greenhorn Limestone** on left in road cut near the vertical dip.

6.1   **Dakota Group and upper Morrison Formation** on the left.   **Late Eocene erosion surface** on skyline at 6:00

6.2   **Dakota Group** in cut to left capped by **Graneros Shale**. On right the Dakota Group trends towards highway indicating end of inlier of Cretaceous rocks and **north end of Twelvemile Park**. The **Precambrian Boulder Creek granodiorite** (1.72 b.y.) will be exposed from here to the junction with CR 112.

6.3   Road generally follows **Current Creek shear zone** exposed in Precambrian rocks for the next 20 miles. A shear zone contains the physically broken and strained rocks on either side of a fault.

6.6   **Microcline megacryst-bearing biotite granite** on left.   **Biotite-quartz-feldspar xenoliths** (inclusions of wall rock in the intrusive) up to four feet long are present. The granite here is mapped as part of the **Cripple Creek batholith** (1.40 to 1.45 b.y.) on the Colorado Geologic Map. The rock type becomes more granodioritic to tonalitic to the north.

6.9   **Sheared biotite granodiorite** on left. Shearing appears stronger and more irregular here and the unit resembles an augen gneiss.

7.4   **Biotite granodiorite gneiss** that is cross cut by **granite**. Xenoliths of granodiorite gneiss are present along the intrusive granite contact.

8.3 **Biotite granodiorite gneiss** interlayered with **biotite schist** on right. Schistosity in the gneiss is vertical.

8.8 Miner's Gulch road to right. Outcrop on left is **biotite-muscovite-plagioclase-quartz schist and gneiss interlayered with quartzite.** Large muscovite spangles on schistocity surfaces are conspicuous.

9.1 **STOP. Metamorphic Rocks.** The unit is **muscovite-plagioclase-quartz schist interlayered with muscovite quartzitic and quartz-chlorite-biotite schist.** This unit is typical of the quartz-rich metasediments. Layering and schistocity are near vertical and show broad warps. The schist is **intruded by pink, muscovite granite and brown-weathering, black diabase.** The metamorphic rocks have an age of 1,700 to 1,800 m. y. The intrusive rocks are part of the **Cripple Creek batholith.**

9.35 **Pegmatite dike** on left.

9.6 **Schist** on left.

10.1 **Thirtynine Mile volcanics** on horizon at 11:00. The smooth rounded topography is typical of the volcanic field.

10.5 On left. **Biotite schist xenoliths in medium-grained biotite granite.**

10.9 **Granite** on left.

11.1 Tallahassee Road to left.

11.5 **Biotite gneiss** on left. Unit is intruded by thin veinlets of pink medium-grained granite.

11.6 Bridge

12.3 **Biotite schist intruded by pegmatite dike** on right.

12.9 Cattle guard. **Biotite schist, gneiss and granite** on right.

14.0 **Interlayered biotite gneiss and granodiorite** on left.

14.1 Cattle guard.

14.7 Hill ahead is **capped by volcanics.** This is **Thirtyone Mile Mountain**, the second center of Oligocene volcanism.

15.5 Cattle guard.

16.4   Granite on right. **Muscovite-quartz-microcline pegmatites** containing accessory **beryl** are exposed on hillside at 3:00.

17.1   **Quartz-rich schist and gneiss** on left. Unit is much like that at last stop.

17.6   **Pegmatite** prospect on right.

18.5   Cattle guard.

19.9   On the right are **biotite-plagioclase-hornblende schist xenoliths** in weathered **medium-grained quartz monzonite**.

20.5   Bridge

20.9   **Interlayered schist and gneiss**.

21.1   Cattle guard.

21.6   Approximate **southern edge of caldera of Guffey volcano**. Please see Geologic History Figure 10.

21.7   Junction with CR 102. Guffey is 1 ½ miles to right. Continue on Colorado Highway 9. There is a separate road log for CR 102 from Guffey to Florissant.

21.8   Cattle guard.

22.3   **Feldspathic gneiss** on right.

23.0   CR 88 to left.

23.5   Road cuts in **Thirtynine Mile volcanics.** Approximate north boundary of caldera of Guffey Center in hills ahead.

23.9   On left, flow **banded and slickensided sanidine trachyte porphyry**.

25.2   **Biotite granite with local gneissic and pegmatitic zones** on left. These **Precambrian rocks are below the volcanic pile.**

26.2   **Gneiss and schist intruded by granite**.

27.0   **Quartz core of a pegmatite dike** on right.

27.1   Purple-weathering **volcanic andesite** on right. **Thirtynine Mile Mountain** at 1:00-2:00 is 3,000 feet of north-dipping mudflows and occasional ignimbrites. This is the **north flank of the Guffey Volcano.**

C 9 Figure 2. At MP 27.1. Looking east at south flank of Thirtynine Mile Mountain. Approximately 3,000 feet of north-dipping (10 degrees) mud flows, with occasional ignimbrites from another source, are exposed in this part of the north flank of the Guffey Volcano.

27.8   Cattle guard. **Precambrian rocks** are exposed to north.

28.3   **Volcanics in float** within park area.

29.5   To the right is purple andesite **mudflow breccia**. A brown-weathering **andesite dike cuts the breccia.**

29.5   Brown-weathering, **black gabbro** on right. **Andesite breccias** underlie the park area to the north.

30.4   Cattle guard.

31.6   On right. Purple and red **andesite breccias (mudflows) intermixed with volcanic ash beds.**

31.7   **Currant Creek Pass** 9,470 feet. **Entering South Park. Threemile Mountain** at 1:00 is composed of **north-northwest dipping mudflows and ash** of this **flank of the Guffey Volcano. Currant Creek Fault** trends northwest immediately east of the pass. From the Hartsel area north it is called the **South Park Fault.** It is a **reverse**

fault with the east side thrust up and over the west. The age of the fault is primarily Laramide, with local areas of Late Tertiary rejuvenation.

Enter South Park. In the **foreground are volcanics** (dominantly andesite breccia). In the background is the **Mosquito Range**. They are **fault block mountains** of Precambrian and Paleozoic rocks intruded by Late Cretaceous, Early and Middle Tertiary igneous rocks. Much of the Mosquito Range above 10,000' was glaciated during the last 1.6 m.y.

32.0   Cattle guard.

33.1 to 33.4. Outcrop across creek to right is **andesite breccia**. The section in this area is described as the "lower andesite" by Chapin and Epis (1964, p.147-149).

33.9   Cattle guard.

34.1   Brown-weathering **andesite porphyry** on right.

35.9   **Andesite mudflow breccia**. This is antelope country.

37.1   Cattle guard.

41.1   One hundred yards up hill on left is yellow-brown-weathering, gray **tuffaceous, sanidine porphyry showing good flow structure**. This is the **Wall Mountain Tuff.**

43.2   Driving on **Balfour Formation** of Late-Eocene or early Oligocene age. This formation contains the earliest volcanic deposits of this area.

45.8   CR 53 to left. There is a separate road log for this road as it crosses the **Antero Syncline.**

46.5   Hill to left mapped as **Denver Formation** (now called **South Park Formation**) by Ettinger (1964. Fig. 1).

47.2   Highway is parallel to **Hartsel Ridge** (on left). Road is on **Morrison Formation,** which is separated from the **Precambrian** on the ridge by the **South Park fault**, a north continuation of the Current Creek fault.

47.9   Junction with U. S. Highway 24, turn left through Hartsel. Road is on **Morrison Formation**. After turn low hills at 10:00 are **Precambrian rocks**. The Hartsel area was a summer destination of Mountain Utes who frequented the hot springs and hunted large herds of buffalo, elk, and other game. In 1862, Sam Hartsel homesteaded 160 acres near the confluence of the South and Middle forks of the South Platte River, two miles east of town. This ranch expanded to 200,000 acres and became one of the most successful cattle ranches in Colorado.

48.3 **Garo Sandstone** on left. **Morrison Formation** in road cut on right. The **Dakota Sandstone** hogback is above the Morrison.

48.4 Bridge. **Dakota Sandstone** on right.

48.6 **Biotite granite** on left. Road is on **Garo Sandstone**. Meandering trout stream (**South Fork of Platte River**) on right. Note that there is **no Maroon Formation redbeds** exposed here. See US Highway 24 Road Log for further discussion.

47.7 Note **correction of mileage** to agree with posted mileage. Junction US Highway 24 with Colorado Highway 9, turn right towards Fairplay.

47.8 Bridge. **Buffalo Peaks** (see US Highway 285 road log) due west. Excellent view of **Mosquito Range** at 10:00 to 12:00. Low red hills ¼ mile west are underlain by **Maroon Formation**.

48.0 Crossing upper part of **Maroon Formation**.

48.3 **Morrison Formation** poorly exposed under **Dakota Sandstone hogback** to right.

48.6 **Upper Maroon conglomerates** in road cut to right. Note that at this point we are about two miles west of the Late Paleozoic Ancestral Front Range.

49.0 Mt. Yale, in the southern part of the Sawatch Range, is visible at 9:00. Mounts Princeton and Antero at 8:30.

49.2 Poorly exposed outcrops of **Maroon Formation** at road level, overlain by bench-forming **Garo Sandstone**. Ridge on skyline to right is **Red Hill (Dakota Sandstone hogback).**

49.8 On right, **Garo Sandstone** outcrops above **Maroon Formation.**

50.3 Ranch on left.

50.8 **Mt. Bross** at 12:00 is northwest of the town of Alma. It is capped by an igneous sill.

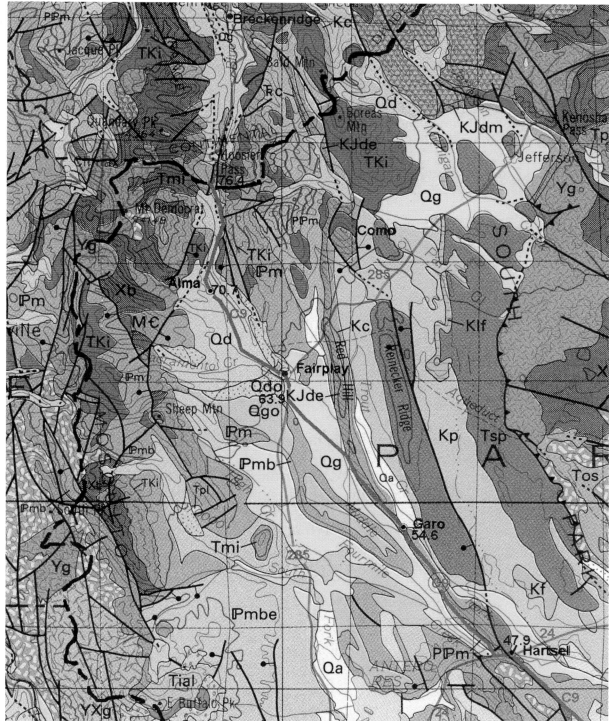

C 9 Figure 3. Geologic Map with route of road log. From Tweto, 1979. Please see Geologic History Figure 1 for an explanation of symbols.

51.3 The northern part of the **Mosquito Range** is visible on the skyline from 10:00 to 11:00. This part of the range consists of **east-dipping Paleozoic sediments cut by east-dipping high angle reverse faults** such as the London and Sherman faults. **Many sills and several stocks** intrude the Paleozoic section.

52.7   Augustine's Holiday Hereford Ranch. Hills at 11:00 are **Maroon Formation**.

53.4   **Garo Sandstone** on right. East-dipping **Dakota Sandstone** at crest of hill.

54.6   Garo Townsite, **type locality of the Garo Sandstone**. One mile south of town a deposit of uranium-vanadium and copper minerals occurs in faulted sandstones of the Maroon Formation (USGS Bulletin 1087-A)

54.9   Bridge over Middle Fork of South Platte River.

55.0   Bridge

55.2   Hill at right covered by **float of Garo Sandstone**.

55.9   Road to right. **Stop**. Suggest that you park about 100 yards from highway and walk across **Red Hill hogback**. **Garo Sandstone, Morrison Formation and Dakota Sandstone** are exposed from west to east. **East of the hogback** there is an excellent view of **Trout Creek Valley** and the **southern part of Reinecker Ridge**. See US Highway 285 Road Log for discussion of the mudflow deposits of Reinecker Ridge. The view from the top of this ridge provides an excellent opportunity to observe the **Geologic Wonders** of South Park. In every direction the mountains are of different ages and origins.

57.5   **Terrace** west of valley at 10:00 is **underlain by Maroon Formation** red beds.

59.9   Bridge. **Mt. Silverheels** at 1:00. Mountain is **east-dipping Maroon Formation intruded by many sills from a stock** immediately north of the mountain in Montgomery Gulch (Singewald, 1942, USGS Bulletin 928-A). The mountain is immediately southwest of the Beaver-Tarryall mining district.

62.0   **Maroon Formation** at 10:00.

62.5   Road is on **glacial outwash of Wisconsin age**.

62.7   **Extensive placer tailings** at 1:00 to 2:00. A gold dredge worked this area of glacial outwash from 1941 to 1952. It mined about 33.5 million cubic yards of gravel from which it extracted around 115,000 ounces of gold. The outwash aprons were the most productive for placer gold. Next were the terminal moraines and then the Alma and Bristol substage terminal moraines (Singewald, 1950).

63.7   Junction Colorado 9 with US Highway 285. Turn right toward Fairplay.

64.0   The aspen and conifer-covered ridges to left of road are underlain by **Illinoian-stage glacial terminal moraine** deposits.

64.6   Middle Fork of South Platte River.

64.7   Junction Colorado 9 and US Highway 285, turn left into Fairplay. In 1859, prospectors already established in the Tarryall Mining District did not welcome newcomers. These late-arriving gold rush types pressed west, established a new camp on the banks of the South Platte River, and called it *Fair Play*. South Park Museum in Fairplay is an authentic reproduction of a 19th century mining town. It includes 32 buildings that were moved there and over 60,000 artifacts that typify the trades, professions and colorful mountain style of the late 1800's.

65.3   Old County Court House, now the county library.

65.5   Climbing hill. Outcrops to right are **Maroon Formation**.

66.0   Top of hill. **Stop** in parking area to left. Here we are on the **crest of the Wisconsin stage terminal moraine**. Note gravel pit and gold placer on west side of river. Reason for stop is to study view to south across South Park. Skyline beyond the Red Hill hogback from east to west includes the **east slope of Saddle Mountain** (10,734 feet), **square top of Thirtynine Mile Mountains**, which is underlain by north dipping volcanic deposits), and farther west, the **west slope of the top of Black Mountain** (11,654 feet). Together these mountains provide the profile of the lower part of the **Guffey Volcano**. On the cover of this book an upper part of a current volcano has been added to reconstruct what the Guffey Volcano looked like during Oligocene time.

The **terminal moraine** here is the **maximum stage of Wisconsin glaciation**. It is the **end of a composite valley glacier fed by glaciers from Sacramento, Mosquito and Buckskin Creeks and Platte Gulch** at the head of the Middle Fork of the South Platte River. The **outwash** from this composite glacier extended south to Hartsel. There is an excellent view of the **outwash-filled valley** from this point.

67.0   CR 14, Sacramento Creek road to left. In the early 1840's, a sizable Ute Indian village was located here. To celebrate the summer's bounty a great feast was held each September before moving east of the Front Range for the winter. Truces with rival tribes were called so that gambling, trading and the purchase of wives could proceed.

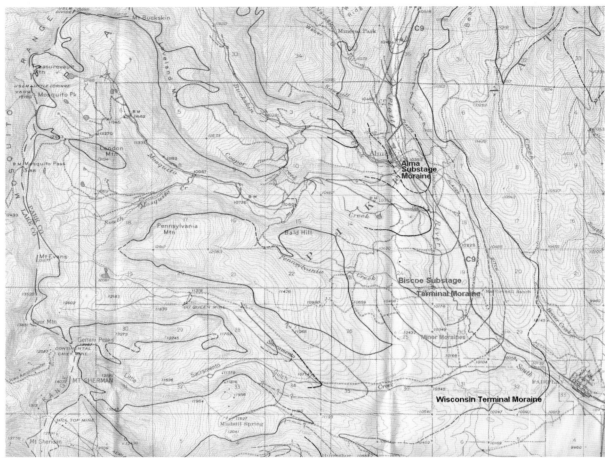

C 9 Figure 4. Map of Wisconsin glacial features between Fairplay and Alma. Purple lines show both the upper and lower extent of glaciation during the Wisconsin stage (last 50,000 years). Other colored lines show limit of substage terminal moraines formed by periods of resurgence during the over all retreat of the glaciers from 25000 to 13000 years ago, after Singewald, 1950, USGS Bulletin 955-D.

69.5   CR 1 to left. Road is now on **Briscoe substage terminal moraine**. To right is the **Snowstorm placer mine**. There is a gold dredge on the property, but it isn't used. Gravel from the east side of the terminal moraine is moved by front-end loader and truck and then fed through a very large sluice box. A by-product is gravel used as construction material. For a detailed discussion of glacial features, deposits and placers please see Singleton, 1950 (especially plates 9 and 10).

69.5   CR 12 to left. Road climbs to **Mosquito Pass** at 13,186 feet (in part strictly four-wheel drive). A separate road log is included in this book. Excellent exposures of **Precambrian igneous and metamorphic rocks**, **Paleozoic sedimentary rocks**, and **Late Cretaceous-Early Tertiary intrusive igneous rocks** are present along the road. The **London fault** is spectacular where it cuts through the middle of London Mountain.

70.4   Cross Middle Fork of South Platte River, enter Alma. Now on **Alma substage terminal moraine**. Placer workings of terminal moraine are east of highway. Note that this moraine is different from the Fairplay and Briscoe moraines. The first two are hummocky and contain a high percentage of fine clastics. The Alma substage moraine is a low smoothly rounded hill nearly a mile long and parallel with the valley (Singleton, 1950, p.155-156). There is no prominent terminal feature and the total deposit is very course material with a small percentage of fine clastics. If you read Singleton you'll find that this is one area where you dig the "**yellow dirt**". That is, the fine **particles of gold in the gravels are associated with grains of magnetite**, which on weathering, give a **yellow limonitic stain** to the pay section. Note that all the placers of the valley are on the **east side**, reflecting a **source from lode gold** that resulted in gold-rich moraines along the east side of the glaciers. Looking up valley, the gold must have come from the south flank of **North Star Mountain**, west of Hoosier Pass.

70.7   Center of Alma. CR 8 to left goes up **Buckskin Gulch**. Three miles in there is a fork with CR 8 continuing on to the Sweet Home Mine and Kite Lake and CR 787 to the right to Mineral Park mining area, **Windy Ridge** with its spectacular bristlecone pines and on past the Dolly Varden Mine **to the top of Mt. Bross** at 14,172 feet. It is four-wheel drive past Mineral Park. Exposures and Geologic Wonders are sufficient to merit separate road logs in this book.

Alma came into existence in the 1870's as a result of a silver rush that was precipitated by new refining technology. A mill was built just north of town and Alma became a refining center for the area. After the silver played out, hydraulic operations to remove gold from the Alma Substage Terminal Moraine gravels sustained Alma well into the 20th century.

71.6   Cross Middle Fork of South Platte River.

71.7   To the left and across the river foundations and some tailings are the remains of the Moose Mining Company headquarters and ore reduction works. The Moose Mine, discovered in 1871 on the east side of Mount Bross at 13,860 feet was the first productive silver mine in Colorado. Rich ore was also found on Mount Lincoln.

72.0   **Minor substage moraine** across valley.

72.5   **Two minor substage moraines** cross valley. **Windy Ridge** above the west side of the valley is the designated **Bristlecone Pine Scenic Area**. The ridge is just a few hundred feet above the **lateral moraine deposits** of the valley glaciers. At 3:00, bristlecone pines are also found across the top of Beaver Ridge.

C 9 Figure 5. Bristle cone pines along Windy Ridge. View is to the south with Alma in the right middle ground and the Briscoe and Wisconsin terminal moraines visible far down the valley.

C 9 Figure 6. Another view of bristle cone pines along Windy Ridge. View is to east across the South Platte valley at Mount Silverheels, which is capped by igneous sills intruded into east-dipping Maroon red beds.

72.7   CR 9 to left. Road starts climb to Hoosier Pass. Road cuts have poor exposures of the lower part of the Pennsylvanian **age Belden shale and Maroon Formation.** Note that most of the hillside has a **thin cover of lateral moraine** deposits that are involved in **soil creep and/or landslides.**

73.2   On right, **thin sill of Lincoln Porphyry** in **Belden** black shale and limestone.

74.5   **Sill** on right.

74.8   **Highway crosses active landslide**. The highway department frequently rebuilds this section to keep up with a slow slide. Some rainy day the whole section will disappear downhill. **Cross with caution**, especially on wet nights!

75.0   Highway crosses **lateral moraine deposits** of this side of the South Platte Valley

C 9 Figure 7. At MP 75.9. View across Montgomery Reservoir at Mount Lincoln on left and upper Platte Valley (Platte Gulch) on right. On the near slope of Mount Lincoln there is an active rock glacier in a hanging valley named the Lincoln Amphitheater. Recommend a climb from the upper end of Montgomery Reservoir to visit this feature.

75.3   CR 4 to left to **Montgomery Reservoir** and upper valley.

75.9   **Stop** on left. **View of upper part of Platte Gulch and Montgomery Reservoir.** There is a tunnel through the Continental Divide that diverts water from the Blue River Drainage to this reservoir for the benefit of Colorado Springs. The valley above the reservoir is a **classic U-shaped glaciated valley**. **Mt. Lincoln** (14,286 feet) is to the left of this valley. The Russian Mine and Quartzville town site are on the southeast flank of the mountain above the timberline.

On the **northeast side of Mt. Lincoln** is our favorite **hanging valley: the Lincoln Amphitheater**. It is a **small cirque that is now occupied by an active rock glacier**. Note the steeply dipping front of the rock glacier. A challenging climb is recommended from the upstream end of Montgomery Reservoir to the hanging valley. Be careful if you climb the front of the rock glacier. It is very unstable and tends to bury one when disturbed.

The town site of Montgomery, now at the bottom of the reservoir, was once the hub of an active mining district formed in 1861. Mining operations dwindled by 1866.

C 9 Figure 8. View north from saddle between Mount Lincoln and Mount Cameron of glaciated terrain at head of Platte Gulch. The Upper and Lower Wheeler Lakes are cirque lakes. The trail to Lower Wheeler Lake is an extreme 4-wheel drive road.

76.4   **Hoosier Pass**. Elevation 11,539 feet. **Continental Divide**. Leaving South Park and Park County. Note that the glaciers spilled over the pass to join a glacier of the Blue River drainage. Poor exposures of lower Maroon on east side of the pass and of a sill of Lincoln porphyry on the west side. To the west along the south side of North Star Mountain there are a number of lode gold mines. They were connected by cable tramway with a mill just west of Montgomery Reservoir.

Wildlife, Indians, fur trappers, and mountain men used the Hoosier Pass area. Gold seekers far from Indiana named this pass. In 1843, John C. Fremont led an expedition through the pass.

According to R. H. Mohlenbrock, 1994, tundra on Hoosier Ridge to the east of the pass is the home of a suite of rare arctic flowers whose relatives are found in places like the Northwest Territories and northern Siberia. When hiking there, please walk softly and definitely don't pick the flowers!

End of Road Log.

C9 Figure 9. Looking south across the cirque lake in the large cirque on the east side of
Horseshoe Mountain. There is a rock glacier in the middle ground. Several faults displace
sills and Paleozoic rock on the skyline.

Mosquito Gulch to Mosquito Pass Road Log
Park County Road 12 and Pike Forest Road 12
Alma Junction to Park City, London Mountain, and Mosquito Pass

Mileage
From
Colorado 9

0.0   Leave Colorado Highway 9 on Mosquito Creek Road, CR 12. Road is on Quaternary **alluvium**. **Pennsylvania Mountain** (13,006 feet) is at 12:00, **London Mountain** (13,194 feet) at 12:30, **Loveland Mountain** (13,560 feet) at 1:00 and **Mount Bross** (14,192 feet) at 2:00.

0.1   **Middle Fork of South Platte River**.

0.2   Climbing front of **Alma substage terminal moraine** at Alma Junction, northern terminus of Denver, South Park and Pacific Railroad. Old railroad wye ("Y-shaped turn-around) can be seen between the river and the highway.

0.9   Crossing **minor substage moraine.**

1.2   Entering a basin that was a **moraine-dammed lake** for a while. Note **scar** high on Pennsylvania Mountain at 10:30. This is a placer mine that will also be visible farther down CR 12. It is a unique deposit of pre-glacial gravel on eroded Lower Paleozoic rocks. The location of this gravel downslope (at time of deposition) from the lode gold of the London Mountain area has resulted in the mining of some of the largest nuggets found in Colorado. One very large gold nugget can be viewed in the Denver Natural History Museum Gem and Mineral Exhibit.

1.7   Kootchi-Kootchi Road to left.

2.2   **Park City.** Please drive slowly. A very rich mining district, including the Orphan Boy Mine, is located along the ridge north of Park City that separates this area from Buckskin Gulch. Park City was a stage stop on the route to Leadville via Mosquito Pass. At its peak there were 300 residents.

       The contact between the Leadville and Weber Formations underlies Park City, but is not visible because of glacial deposits. For the next 0.6 miles the road crosses the buried outcrops of the east-dipping (10-20 degrees) Lower Paleozoic section.

	Explanation of symbols for Mosquito Creek and Buckskin Gulch Road Log Maps.	
	Younger Intrusive Igneous rocks	
Tgp	Granodiorite, porphyritic facies (? m.y.)	
Tqm	Quartz monzonite porphyry (42 m.y. at Peak Nine, Zartman, et al, 1995)	
Tmd	Monzonite-diorite porphyry (67 m.y.?, Late Cretaceous)	
Tlw	Later white porphyry	
Tgd	Granodiorite of Buckskin Gulch Stock (70 m.y., Misantoni, 2001 personal communication)	
Tlp	Lincoln porphyry (70 m.y.?, Late Cretaceous)	
Tew	White Porphyry (71 m.y.?, Late Cretaceous)	
	Sedimentary Rocks	
Cw	Pennsylvanian Weber Formation	
Cl	Mississippian Leadville Limestone	
Cld	Leadville Limestone and Dyer Dolomite	
Dd	Devonian Dyer Dolomite	
Dpq	Devonian Parting Quartzite	
Om	Ordovician Manitou Limestone and upper part of Peerless Shale Member of Sawatch Formation (Upper Cambrian)	
Cs	Cambrian Sawatch Quartzite	
	Uncomformity	
	Precambrian Igneous and Metamorphic Rocks	
pt	Pegmatite dikes	
spg	Silver Plume granite	
ppg	Pikes Peak Granite (probably misidentified and should be granite)	
grg	Granite gneiss	
sch	schist and injection gneiss	

2.5   **Minor substage terminal moraine.** Hill at 9:00 is **Bald Hill,** 11,428 feet. The north flank of Bald Hill is a series of **lateral moraines** deposited by successive glaciers that moved down Mosquito Creek. Glaciers did not cover Bald Hill or Pennsylvania Mountain.

3.0   Road to left leads to a **placer mine** high on the northeast flank of Pennsylvania Mountain. At 9:00, the mine low on the north flank of Pennsylvania Mountain is one of many observable on both sides of CR 12.

3.6   High at 9:00. **Pennsylvania Mountain**, 13,006 feet. In the valley wall there are excellent exposures of **Precambrian-Lower Paleozoic contact and of the Lower Paleozoic section**. At 3:00 the same section is exposed on Loveland **Mountain**, 13,600 feet. There is **glacial polish** high on the south side of the valley. **London Mountain**, 13,194 feet, is straight ahead.

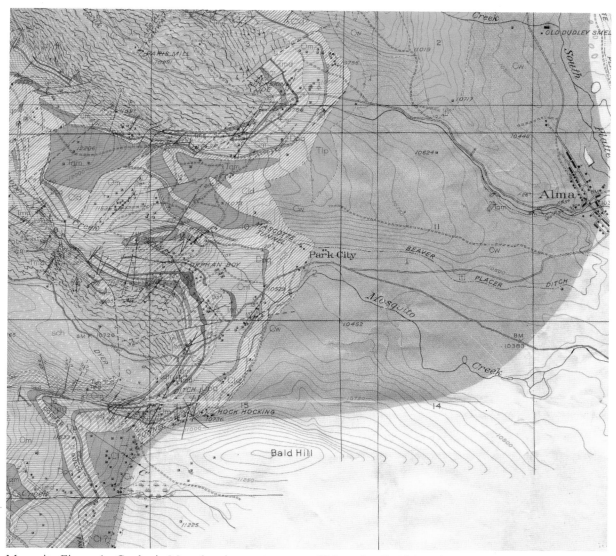

Mosquito Figure 1. Geologic Map showing eastern part of Mosquito Creek Road. From Singewald, 1941, Plate 1.

4.2   At 9:00 across valley: Glaciers polished Precambrian rocks of the valley wall.

4.3   **Precambrian gneiss** outcrop on right.

4.4   Y in road, bear right. Left fork leads to **London Mine** at southeast base of London Mountain and the **London Extension** and **Butte Mines** of the northwest flank of Pennsylvania Mountain. Collectively these mines, along with the London Mine, were active until 1990 when the price of gold fell below the extraction cost (about $370/once.) At the time of shutdown the mine employed 9 men.

4.5   CR 12 crosses a **landslide**. Caution, there are fresh slides each year.

5.6   Road to left leads to the mill of the American Mine across the valley. The buildings at the mine were repainted during the "80's" and tailings were sent to a refinery. The investors would get some "shows" from the tailings, but nothing commercial. Looks like a masterful scam, but don't know real story.

Starting Pike National Forest Road 12. Road is rough and not maintained from this point.

5.7   **Upper glaciated valley of Mosquito Creek.**

Mosquito Figure 2. At MP 4.5. View at 9:00 of northwest edge of Pennsylvania Mountain. Precambrian metamorphic rocks were smoothed and polished by the valley glaciers that flowed past this point.

6.3   At 10:30. Old buildings of the **mill for the North London Mine**. A **cable tramway** connected them, and remnants are still visible. This 3,300-foot tramway was the first constructed in Colorado. There is an environmental problem with mercury in the gravels downstream from this mill.

6.8   Left turn and cross **Mosquito Creek**. Unless there has been some improvement, **this is the end of the road for low clearance vehicles**. Definitely four-wheel drive or hiking from here to pass. Well worth the hike!

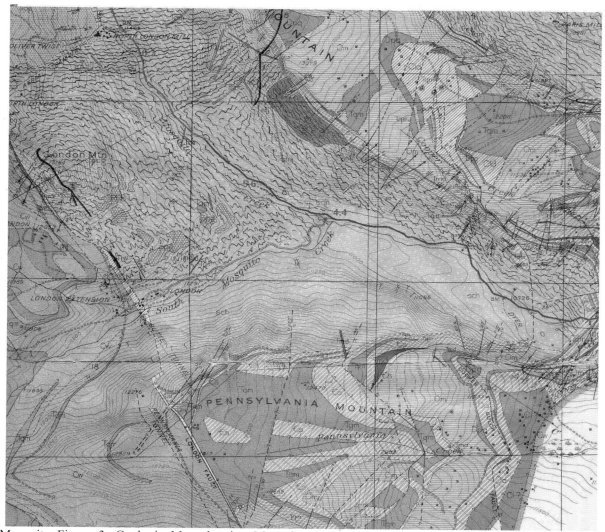

Mosquito Figure 3. Geologic Map showing Mosquito Creek Road northeast of London Mountain. From Singewald, 1941, Plate 1. See Mosquito Figure 1 for explanation of symbols.

6.9 **Mosquito Pass Wagon Road sign**. In 1879, a group of investors that included Horace Tabor formed the Mosquito Pass Wagon Road Company. The discovery of silver at Leadville spurred the construction of the road across Mosquito Pass. This route, although narrow, steep, and treacherous was the preferred route because it was only 22 miles from Fairplay to Leadville as compared with 40 miles via Weston Pass and 72 miles along Trout Creek. There was a Half Way House with saloon, stables, and store at this point that served dinners for 50 cents. The buildings were erased by a snow slide in 1890.

7.0 Hairpin turn to steep part of road. A **short stop** here is in order to see the **beaver dams** and **glacial features**. Hidden out of view around the highest parts of the valley are cirques, most of which have small cirque lakes. Road in this area is on **Silver Plume Granite (1,430 m.y.),** which can be seen in float. This granite intrusive is called the **Treasurevault Stock**. There is no mineralization attributed to this stock.

Figure Mosquito 4. At MP 6.3. Old buildings of the mill for the North London Mine. Note scar of cable tramway. A branch of the railroad served this mill in the 1880 and 1890's. The mill still operated in the 1930's.

7.2   On either side of the road there is a **beautiful flower garden**, especially in early summer. Every type of alpine flower is in abundance. Take pictures but please do not pick!

7.7   At 12:00 **London Mountain**, 13,194 feet. Note the excellent exposure of the **London Fault** cutting through the middle of the mountain. **Precambrian metamorphic rocks** on the east (upthrown) side of the fault; lower Pennsylvanian **Weber Quartzite** on downthrown west side. There is **severe drag at the fault**. This is a **high angle reverse fault** that dips northeast. Look for early white porphyry and quartz monzonite sills intruded into the Weber section. The hydrothermal waters that deposited gold and other minerals from an underlying magma came up along this fault. Most of the gold was deposited where water infiltrated rocks on the downthrown side.

8.1   **North London Mine**. Steep road ahead from mine to the saddle cuts across **Weber Quartzite**.

Mosquito Figure 5. At MP 7.2. View in flower garden. Boulders are Silver Plume Granite from Treasurevault Stock.

Mosquito Figure 6. At MP 7.7. View of London Fault (f) on north flank of London Mountain. This is a reverse fault with Precambrian metamorphic rocks on east (left) side upthrust over near vertical Weber Sandstones. Note change of dip in the Weber Sandstones from near vertical to slightly east dipping from center to right in the north face of the mountain.

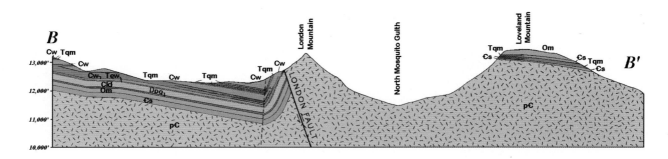

Mosquito Figure 7. West-east cross section from Mosquito Pass through London Mountain to Loveland Mountain. From Singewald, 1941, Plate 2.

Table 1. Generalized Stratigraphic section of the London fault region, Colorado					
Age	Formation and Member		Lithologic Divisions	Thickness (feet)	Character
Pennsylvanian	Weber Formation			4,000	Interbedded Quartzite, conglomerate, grit, arkose, shale, and sparse limestone, all micaceous. Some highly carbonaceous shale. Shale predominates near base, sandy beds in upper part
Mississippian	Leadville Limestone			Limestone	0-100	Blue to black, mostly dense-textured, massive-bedded, dolomitic limestone. Shatters easily. Weathers with pitted surfaces, and breaks into blocky fragments. "Zebra-rock", chert, and limestone breccia are common.
			Quartzite	0-8	Fine-grained to dense "chert-looking" white quartzite. Extremely lenticular.
Upper Devonian	Chaffee Formation	Dyer Dolomite Member	Limestone	40-78	Fairly thin-bedded, mostly dense white and blue dolomitic limestone. White beds weather cream colored. Exposed surfaces generally smooth.
		Parting Quartzite Member		0-55	Cross-bedded and conglomeratic quartzite and sandy limestone, Quartz pebbles subangular. Locally slightly shaly. Weathers light to dark brownish gray.
Lower Devonian	Manitou Limestone		Limestone	0-130	Thin-bedded white and medium-blue, mostly "crystalline" dolomitic limestone. Weathers light gray, developing siliceous ribbing. Breaks to slabby fragments. Locally slightly shaly at top.
Upper Cambrian	Sawatch quartzite	Peerless shale member (Transition shale)	Upper shaly beds	12-27	Interbedded dolomitic limestone, shaly limestone, and limy shale. Limestone weathers brown; shale green.
			Upper limy beds	15-30	Drab-to brownish-weathering limestone, dolomitic and somewhat sandy, with numerous limy-shale partings.
			Lower shaly beds	18-30	Thin-bedded, almost flaggy dolomitic limestone and shale. Upper limestones contain "red casts". Limestone weathers brown; shale green.
			Middle limy beds	15-30	Brownish-weathering dolomitic limestone with numerous shale partings.
			Purple quartzite	2-15	Purple to nearly black quartzite, slightly cross-bedded. Contains tiny angular quartz pebbles.
			Upper white quartzite	6-14	Fairly thick-bedded white fine-grained quartzite.
		Hiatus(?)	Lower limy beds	9-13	Thin-bedded series of quartzite, limy quartzite, sandy limestone, shale, and rare limestone. Weathers brownish and "sandy-looking".
			Lower white quartzite	45-90	Fairly thick-bedded white fine-grained quartzite. A few beds have small quantities of carbonate cement. At base is a white quartzite conglomerate with pebbles less than 1 inch in diameter.
Pre-Cambrian					Schist, injection gneiss, granite, and pegmatite.

Mosquito Figure 8. Generalized section of the London fault region. From Singewald, 1941, Table 1.

8.6 **Stop**. **Saddle** between London Mountain and unnamed peak, 13,556 feet, south of Mosquito Peak, 13,781 feet. At saddle outcrop is **quartz monzonite porphyry** on the west side and **Weber Sandstone** (with some prominent black shale intervals) on the east, London Mountain side. Section from here to Mosquito Pass is Weber Sandstone intruded by quartz monzonite and early white porphyry sills. View to south to **Mount Sherman**, 14,007 feet, Gemini **Peak** 13,857 feet, **Dyer Mountain** 13,855 feet and **Mount Evans** 13,577 feet from **left to right** along the **crest of the Mosquito Range.**

Some of the peaks are capped by sills, others by Lower Paleozoic sediments. In the foreground is a **huge amphitheater** called the **American Flats** where glaciers originated to move down South Mosquito or Sacramento Creeks on either side of Pennsylvania Mountain.

To the southeast the **London Fault** can be traced **along the west side of Pennsylvania Mountain** and southeast eight miles to the **saddle on the west side of Sheep Mountain,** 12,818 feet. All along the trace the **Pennsylvanian Weber Sandstone** is exposed along the southwest downthrown side and **Precambrian and Lower Paleozoic rocks** on the northeast upthrown side.

	TYPE OF ROCK	THICKNESS
	Weber (?) formation, with several quartz monzonite porphyry sills	700'±
	"PORPHYRY ZONE" Interfingering sills of white porphyry and quartz monzonite porphyry, with lenses of Weber (?) formation. Almost everywhere a 10' to 20' layer of Weber (?) shale, quartzite, and locally limestone occurs at the base	175'-275'
	Leadville limestone and Dyer dolomite member of Chaffee formation, containing local sills of porphyry	240'±
	Parting quartzite member of Chaffee formation	20'
	Manitou limestone and upper part of Peerless shale member of Sawatch quartzite; possibly containing porphyry sills	120'±
	Sawatch quartzite (including lower part of Peerless shale member)	135'±
	Pre-Cambrian	

Mosquito Figure 9. Generalized columnar section at London Mountain. From Singewald, 1941, Figure 3.

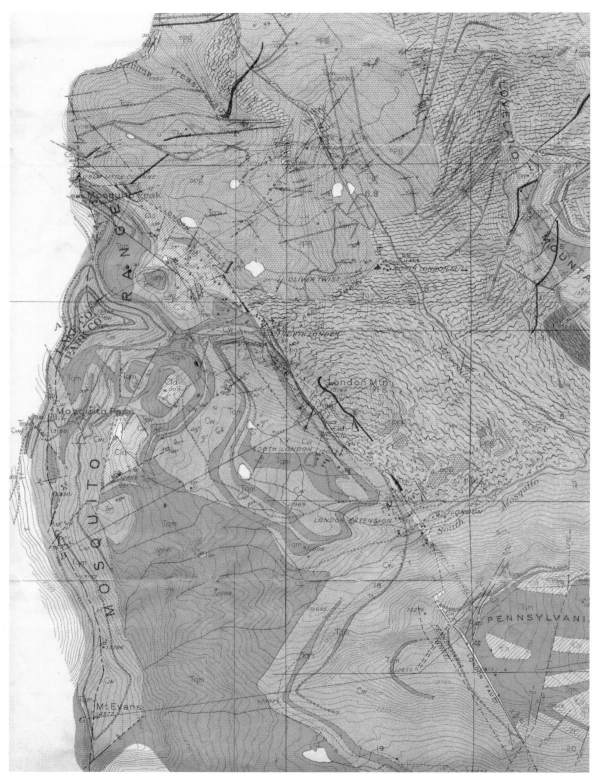

Mosquito Figure 10. Geologic Map showing Mosquito Creek Road from North London Mine to Mosquito Pass. From Singewald, 1941, Plate 1. See Mosquito Figure 1 for explanation of symbols.

Mosquito Figure 11. At MP 8.5. Bighorn sheep on ledge of Weber Sandstone. Part of the herd that lives on London Mountain.

Mosquito Figure 12. At MP 8.6 near saddle. Interbeds of Belden-type black shale in Weber Sandstone section. Singewald (1941) reports that clay gouge in the London fault zone near the base of the Weber provided an upward seal to the migration of mineral-bearing hydrothermal waters. The breakdown to clays of these shales probably were a major contributor to the seal.

Mosquito Figure 13. At MP 8.6. At saddle west of London Mountain, looking southeast across American Flats at the London Fault cut through the west side of Pennsylvania Mountain. Weber Sandstone on the right, southwest side of the fault, Precambrian and Lower Paleozoic rocks on the left. A hydrothermally altered zone marks the fault trace

Mosquito Figure 14. At MP 9.5. Thistle growing in Weber Sandstone talus.

Mosquito Figure 15. At MP 9.6. London Mountain from the west.

9.5 **Quartz monzonite porphyry sill** on right. Note Weber Quartzite and porphyry in **talus** (loose rocks) along road. Singewald (1941) reports that 90 percent of the gold found under London Mountain was in veins "in or adjacent to two continuous sills of white porphyry and quartz monzonite porphyry that are very close to the base of the Weber Formation." This sill appears to be a continuation of the upper sill.

9.7 **Mosquito Pass,** 13,186 feet. Turn left and drive south along this part of the crest of the Mosquito Range.

9.9 Parking area on knoll along the crest of the ridge. Spectacular view of **Mosquito Fault, Leadville Mining District, London Mountain and Fault, Sawatch Range, and Upper Arkansas Valley (north end of Rio Grande Rift).** It is interesting to note that the peaks of the Mosquito Range are sills and Lower Paleozoic rocks that are resistant to erosion, while the Precambrian rocks between the peaks and the **Mosquito Fault** are more easily eroded and form a relative topographic low. There is an excellent map and description of this area and the Leadville Mining District in Behre, 1953 *Geology and Ore Deposits of the West Slope of the Mosquito Range,* USGS Professional Paper 235.

End of Road Log.

Mosquito Figure 16. At Parking knoll, MP 9.9. View to south of Mosquito Fault. The fault cuts north south on the right side of the picture. Grass-covered slopes on far right are Weber Sandstones and sills west of the fault. Bedded rocks in middle distance are Lower Paleozoic carbonates showing rollover drag against upthrown side of fault. Mount Evans (13,577 feet) is at the upper left. Massive units on the west slope of Mount Evans include a 200-foot thick Early White Porphyry sill and an overlying 500-foot thick Gray Porphyry sill intruded into the Weber Sandstone. Mountains in the right background are part of the Sawatch Range west of the Upper Arkansas rift valley.

Mosquito Figure 17. At parking knoll, MP 9.9. View to west of Leadville and the Upper Arkansas Rift Valley. Mining district is in the left-center, east of Leadville. Independence Pass, northern part of Sawatch Range and Turquoise Lake from left to right in distance.

Buckskin Gulch Road Log
County Road 8, Alma to Kite Lake

Mileage

0.0   Start at cross roads of Colorado 9 and County Road 8 in the middle of Alma, which is the highest incorporated town in North America.

0.1   **V-shaped canyon** in **Weber Sandstones** (Early Pennsylvanian in age) at **mouth of Buckskin Gulch**. How did glacier(s) exit Buckskin Gulch to join South Platte glaciers? This part of the gulch must be post-glacial.

0.5   **Belden Formation** (Lower Pennsylvanian) on the right. Soft sandstones are interbedded with black shale and thin limestones.

0.6   Crossing **Alma substage terminal moraine**. **Lincoln Porphyry sill** in road cut to right is intruded at the base of the Pennsylvanian section. For next 0.3 miles the road crosses an **east dipping Lower Paleozoic section**.

1.4   Now on **Precambrian metamorphic rocks**. Site of **Buckskin** to right, **placer workings to left**. Silverheels was a dance hall girl in Buckskin in the 1860's. She cared for miners stricken with smallpox during an epidemic until she caught and was disfigured by the pox. She was never seen after that event. No one knew her given name, only her stage name.

1.5   Road to right to Buckskin Cemetery. Interesting head stones.

1.7   Road to left leads to the **Park City mining district,** which lies in a faulted and intruded Lower Paleozoic section on the ridge between Buckskin Gulch and Mosquito Creek.

1.8   **Minor substage terminal moraines** (three in next half mile)

2.5   **Arrastra wheel** at stream level on left. This was a mule-powered ore crusher dating back to the 1860's.

2.7   **Stop. Paris Mill.** This mill for processing ores was connected by **aerial tramways** both to the north and southwest. The end of the southwest tramway is at the **Precambrian-Cambrian contact** near the crest of the ridge of **Loveland Mountain**. Note the **fault** near the southwest end.

Buckskin Figure 1. Geologic map showing road from Buckskin to Kite Lake. From Singewald, 1941. Plate 1. See Mosquito Figure 1 for explanation of symbols. Buckskin Gulch Stock is labeled Tgd.

Buckskin Figure 2. At MP 2.7. View across Paris Mill at faulting on southeast side of Loveland Mountain.

2.8   CR 787 to right follows the contour around **Mount Bross** to **Mineral Park.** A separate Road Log describes the Lower Paleozoic section traversed. The road is near the Leadville-Weber contact along the east side of Mount Bross. From Mineral Park it is four-wheel drive to **Windy Ridge Bristlecone Scenic Area** (access is restricted). Beyond that point, the road climbs through many prospects (some exploring a known **molybdenum deposit**) on the east side of Mount Bross to the top of the mountain. A Lincoln Porphyry sill caps Mount Bross and Mount Lincoln.

3.4   **Hanging valley of a tributary glacier** at 10:00. The valley you are in has the **U-shape** of a valley eroded by repeated glacier movements. The **valley glacier** that eroded Buckskin Gulch extended to the South Platte Valley and joined other glaciers from north of Mount Lincoln and from the Mosquito Creek drainage that together extended down to the Fairplay area.

2.7   View of Red Amphitheater, the **hydrothermally altered area** above **Sweet Home mine** on the southwest side of Mount Bross. **Altered area** includes part of the **Buckskin Stock** and **adjacent Precambrian metamorphic rocks**.

3.9   **Buckskin Gulch Stock** at 1:00 to 2:00 above Sweet Home Mine.

Buckskin Figure 3. At MP 3.6. View of **Red Amphitheater. Hydrothermal waters caused the highly altered area** above **Sweet Home mine** on the southwest side of Mount Bross.

4.0   **Sweet Home Mine** on right. This was an **old silver mine** that was reopened in 1990 to mine **rhodochrosite and associated crystals.** A reproduction of this mine greets one on entry to the **Gem and Mineral Exhibit of the Denver Natural History Museum.** They also have a six-inch rhodochrosite crystal on display that is the largest ever found. The crystals were deposited in open pockets in metamorphic rocks by hydrothermal waters around the Buckskin stock. Dean Misantoni (2001, personal communication) advises that the stock is the oldest of the Laramide intrusives (70 m.y.?) in this district, while the hydrothermal deposition of crystals in the contact metamorphic zone around the stock is dated at 30.6 to 27.6 my. The age of the silver-lead mineralization is unknown. The Climax molybdenite-bearing stock, three miles northwest of Buckskin Gulch, is dated at 30 m.y. (Zortman, 1995) indicating that the rhodochrosite suite of minerals is related to that event and not to the Buckskin Stock emplacement. There is an excellent publication on the Sweet Home Mine that discusses the history and geology of this area and shows pictures of the beautiful crystals taken from this mine. (Moore, et al, 1998)

Buckskin Figure 4. Example of spectacular mineral specimens obtained from the Sweet Home Mine. Rhodochrosite with fluorite on tetrahedrite matrix, 13.2 cm. (Moore, 1998.) Photo by Jeff Scovil. Reproduced by courtesy of Mineral Record and photographer.

4.3 Climbing on minor **substage terminal moraine**. This point is on the **south edge of Buckskin granodiorite stock**. **Red Amphitheater** on right. Colors are from hydrothermal alteration of stock and adjacent metamorphic rocks.

Buckskin Figure 5. At MP 4.0. Miners at portal of Sweet Home mine. From left: Scott Betz, Geologist Dean Misantoni, John Price and Nate Arnold.

4.5 **Northwest edge of stock**. **Gneiss** is in contact with the **quartz monzonite** intrusive. Loveland Mountain (13,670 feet) capped by **lower Paleozoic rock intruded by sills** at 8:00, **Buckskin Mountain** (13,858 feet) capped by **gneiss** at 9:00, **Mount Democrat** (14,148 feet) capped by **gneiss** at 12:00, **Mount Cameron** (14,238 feet) capped by **Leadville Limestone** at 1:30 and **Mount Bross** (14,172 feet) capped by **Lincoln Porphyry sill** at 3:00. **Hanging valley of a tributary glacier** at 10:00.

5.2 **Ford.** May need 4-wheel drive or high clearance to cross.

5.7 **Kite Lake** (12,033 feet). Trail to left to Lake Emma (12,624 feet). Both are **cirque lakes. Lower Paleozoic section** along ridge to east. Note many dikes and sills that intrude all parts of the section. Some have been dated at 71 to 67 m.y. (Zartman, 1995).

End of Road Log.

Buckskin Figure 6. Looking across Kite Lake at southwest flank of Mount Cameron. Precambrian-Lower Paleozoic contact near the top of the slope. Light-colored rocks in upper part of Precambrian are part of a pegmatite dike of Precambrian age.

Buckskin Figure 7. View to west from saddle between Mount Bross and Mount Lincoln across glacially carved terrain around Kite Lake.

Windy Ridge Road Log
Paris Mill to Windy Ridge and top of Mount Bross

Mileage

0.0   From the junction CR 8 and CR 787 near Paris Mill go east on CR 787. Traveling across a **lateral moraine**.

0.2   **Gneiss** outcrop on left.

0.3   Small lake on left.

0.5   **Stop.** Good view of **Lower Paleozoic section** in the slope to the left. **Cambrian quartzites** lie unconformably on **Precambrian gneiss** and are overlain by **Ordovician, Devonian and Mississippian limestones.** The mine entrance is at the edge of a **Tertiary monzonite diorite porphyry sill intruded into gneiss** (green symbol on Buckskin Figure 1 from Singewald, 1941, USGS Bulletin 911.)

0.9   **Viewpoint.** Note **terminal moraine north of Fairplay and substage terminal moraines** across South Platte valley. **Thirtynine Mile Volcanic field** can be seen across the south side of South Park. **Pikes Peak** is at 1:00 in the far distance. **Sheep Mountain** is at 4:30. Road is on a **lateral moraine** deposit.

1.0   **Cambrian quartzitic sandstone** on left.

1.4   **Leadville Limestone** in float on left. Rocks in **"float"** are eroded from the underlying bedrock and now are in overlying soils.

1.8   Road is on a **lateral moraine** of the South Platte glacier.

2.3   **Intrusive sill** rock in float.

2.4   **Pennsylvanian sandstone** in float.

2.8   **Mineral Park. May need 4-wheel drive from this point.** The trench on the left is cut in silicified **Leadville Limestone.** Note ruins of ore-processing mill.

3.0   Cross stream, bear right up slope.

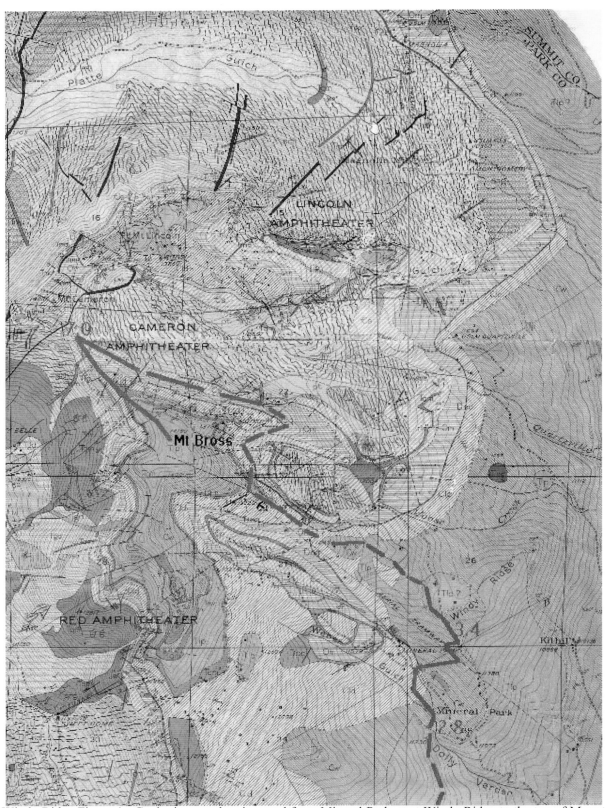

Windy Ridge Figure 1. Geologic map showing road from Mineral Park, past Windy Ridge to the top of Mount Bross. From Singewald, 1941, Plate 1.

3.4   **Windy Ridge** parking area.   Bristlecone pines are on **Pennsylvanian Weber Sandstone** in the southern half of ridge and on a sill of **Lincoln Porphyry** over the northern half.

Windy Ridge Figure2.   Typical wind-molded bristlecone pine.   Sheep Mountain in background.

3.7   Take right fork.

4.3   **Cambrian sandstone.**

4.4   At the curve is a **cirque** at 12:00.   In the walls of the cirque the **Lower Paleozoic section** lies unconformably on **Precambrian gneiss**.

5.1   Curve in road.   Excellent view to the east of **Mount Silverheels (13,822 feet)** and ranges to the north, e.g. **Red Mountain (13,229 feet).**   Outcrops here are **Leadville Limestone.**

5.4   **Cambrian sandstone.**

5.7   Cabin on right.

Windy Ridge Figure 3. Looking down the Middle Fork of the South Platte River valley from Windy Ridge. The town of Alma is in right center of the view. Stumps in foreground are from trees that were cut down during the 1800's for mine timber, cabin construction, fuel, etc.

5.9   **Quartz monzonite porphyry sill**.

6.4   **Mount Lincoln (14,286 feet)** at 1:00 is capped by a Lincoln Porphyry sill. **Cameron Amphitheater (a large cirque)** in between. Excellent view of geologic section on south side of Mount Lincoln.

6.5   **Mine portal** on left.

7.0   **Saddle** between Mount Bross and Mount Cameron, turn left up Bross. Road is on **Cambrian sandstone and Ordovician Manitou Limestone**.

7.3   Climbing through **Lower Paleozoic section with quartz monzonite sills**.

7.5   **Top of Mount Bross (14,172 feet)**. You are parked on **Lincoln Porphyry sill** intruded into sandstones of the Weber Formation. Note very large orthoclase feldspar crystals in the porphyry and beauty of the rock.

End of Road Log.

Windy Ridge Figure 4. Looking north from Mount Bross across Cameron Amphitheater at Mount Lincoln. East-dipping Precambrian-Lower Paleozoic contact in left middle of view. Mount Lincoln is capped by a Lincoln Porphyry sill. Quandary Mountain is in the background.

Windy Ridge Figure 5. Aerial view to northwest over
Alma of Buckskin Gulch and south flank of Mt. Bross.

Boreas Pass Road Log
Park County Road 50 and Summit County Road 10
US Highway 285 to Como, Boreas Pass, and Breckenridge
Parts of this road log taken from Road Log by Gerhard, et al, 1970.

Cumulative
Mileage

0.0   Leave US Highway 285 and start north on CR 50. The road is on a **Late Tertiary terrace** labeled the **Como Surface.**

0.2   On **Como Surface**. At 10:00: the **hill** west of Como with **south-facing cliffs** is a composed of a series of **welded debris flows** (Boreas Figures 1 and 8). Originally, these incandescent flows of angular pieces of lava and volcanic ash were deposited in a valley that was near the parent volcano. Erosion since has removed the surrounding soft rock and left the very hard, resistant igneous rock as a prominent ridge. This deposit is probably the same age as the ignimbrite and mudflow rocks of Reinecker Ridge. Note that both ridges occupy a similar position relative to the surrounding areas.

Boreas Figure 1. Hill west of Como. Entire hill is a series of ignimbrite flows at same elevation and possibly of same age as Reinecker Hill mudflows.

Boreas Figure 2. View from south of Boreas Mountain, center of the Boreas Stock.

0.3   Entering Como. The roundhouse of the Denver, South Park and Pacific Railroad is on the right. The first street to the right leads to general store and the Depot Restaurant. The restaurant has excellent breakfasts and good meals all the time. Como was named in 1879 by Italian coal miners after Lake Como in Italy. Como is near the site of the highest recorded occurrence of the Columbian Mammoth. The bones of *Mammuthus columbi,* an earlier cousin of the woolly mammoth, were discovered near here at an elevation of 9,600 feet. The remains of the mammoth included ribs, vertebrae and a tusk. In addition, two teeth of an extinct species of horse were found at the site. The remains are now exhibited at the **Mammoth Museum** in Como.

In 1873, the Denver, South Park and Pacific Railroad began construction of a route to the mineral areas in South Park. It was a narrow gauge track (three feet between rails; standard gauge is 4 feet 8 ½ inches), which was better suited to the rugged countryside. Construction through Kenosha Pass and into Como occurred in 1879.

0.5   **Turn right**. Follow signs to **Boreas Pass**.

0.7   At 10:00, **Little Baldy Mountain** (12,142 feet). Straight ahead is **Hamilton Mountain** (12,601 feet). Hamilton Mountain is in the southern part of the very large **Boreas stock**. The Little Baldy area is a complexly faulted sequence of steeply east-dipping **Maroon through Benton** sediments that have been **intruded by monzonite porphyry**. The large area of porphyry on the north side of Little Baldy may be a small stock.

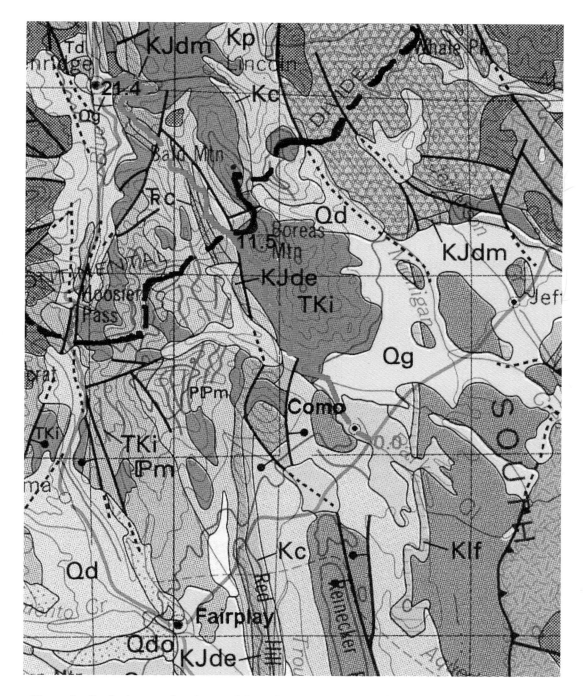

Boreas Figure 3. Geologic map showing road from Como to Breckenridge. Please see Geologic History Figure 1 for an explanation of symbols.

1.1   Cross the abandoned railroad grade. Abandoned **coalmine pilings** can seen to at 10:00. Coal mining started in 1871 and expanded after the arrival of the railroad line in 1879. Coal was mined here and south of US Highway 285 from beds in the lower part of the Late Cretaceous **Laramie Formation**.

1.3   Como cemetery to left.

1.7 To the left above the timberline the east-dipping **Dakota Sandstone** is visible on the east side of the summit. A **Morrison Formation** outcrop may be seen beneath the Dakota.

2.0 Crossing **outwash of Illinoian Stage glaciers**.

2.5 Cross **Tarryall Creek**. The area has been extensively **placer-mined**. Glacial deposits here are mapped as **Illinoian moraine** and **outwash from Wisconsin moraine**. Tarryall Creek was the site of the **first gold discovery** in the Western United States in 1805. However, the first gold rush to the area did not take place until 54 years later when gold was rediscovered on Tarryall Creek.

2.7 Crossing **Illinoian terminal moraine** from here to Peabodies. The **Wisconsin terminal moraine** is one-half mile upstream from Peabodies.

2.8 **Mount Silverheels** (13,822 feet) is straight ahead. See the Buckskin Gulch road log for background on the dance hall girl known as Silverheels. She was an angel to the miners during a small pox epidemic.

3.3 **Talus** on right is from the edge of the **Boreas Stock**.

3.6 Abandoned settlement of Peabodies is on the right.

3.7 Road junction. Leave CR 50, **Turn right** up railroad grade to **Boreas Pass**. Road to left is to **Beaver-Tarryall Mining District**. (The road terminates in 2.7 miles at a locked gate on land owned by Amon C. Carter.) Please see 1942 report by Q. D. Singewald in U. S. Geologic Survey Bulletin 928-A on the bedrock and glacial geology of this area. The **main mining area** is in **Montgomery Gulch,** which is immediately north of Mount Silverheels. The **mineralized area** is characterized by **contact metamorphism** around a **monzonite stock** and many sills are intruded into steeply east-dipping (20-40 degrees) Maroon sediments.

4.0 Outcrop of the southern edge of the **Boreas quartz monzonite stock** above settlement of Peabodies. Dates of samples from railroad cuts into stock range from 44 to 41 my. (Zortman, 1995).

4.2 View across the northeast part of South Park. **Tarryall** and **Kenosha Mountains** of the Front Range are on the skyline.

5.4 **Davis Overlook. Stop.** Excellent outcrops of **quartz monzonite** of the southwest part of **Boreas stock** are visible. The intrusive rocks of the Boreas stock are dated as **Eocene**. Extrusive representatives are believed present in the South Park Formation.

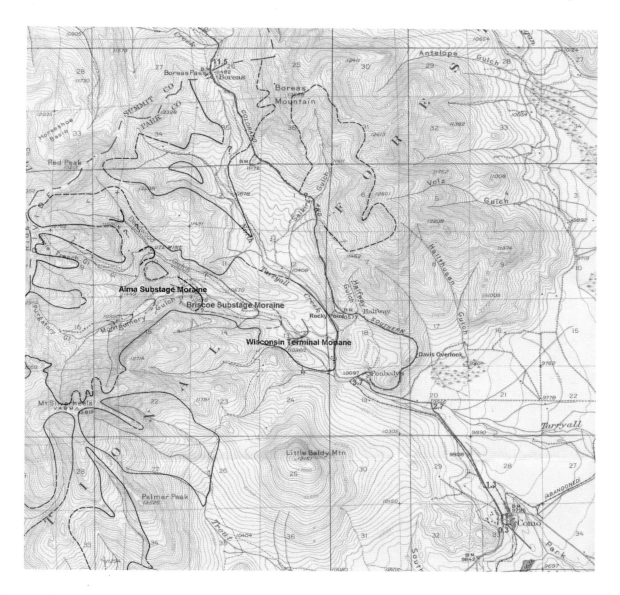

Boreas Figure 4. Map showing Wisconsin Glacial Features. Please See C9 Road Log Figure 6 for an explanation of lines. From Singewald, 1950, Plate 9.

From Peabodies to Boreas Pass the road follows the abandoned Denver, South Park and Pacific Railroad. The US Army Corps of Engineers reworked the railroad bed for automobile traffic in 1950's. This overlook was named for Grover G. Davis, a young dozer operator killed during construction of the road.

There is a **Late Tertiary (Como) surface** in the park. At a slightly higher elevation there is the more prominent and widespread **Late Eocene surface.** This surface extends across the hummocky terrain over the **Elkhorn overthrust** and dominates the **profile of the Front Range** north of Pikes Peak. The **trace** of the **Elkhorn thrust** is marked by the change in vegetation and topography from pine-covered and hummocky hills over the thrust to low relief grasslands west of the trust (Please see Elkhorn Figure 4).

Boreas Figure 5. MP 6.45. View southwest from Rocky Point. Looking at northeast flank of Little Baldy Mountain. North part of the mountain is monzonite porphyry that may be a small stock. Placer workings in foreground are in Wisconsin Terminal Moraine.

Boreas Figure 6. At MP 9.3. Looking west at Montgomery Gulch. Mount Silverheels is on the left. Singewald (1942) maps the Montgomery Stock in the valley north of Mount Silverheels. The gold bearing veins were found in a contact metamorphic zone around this stock.

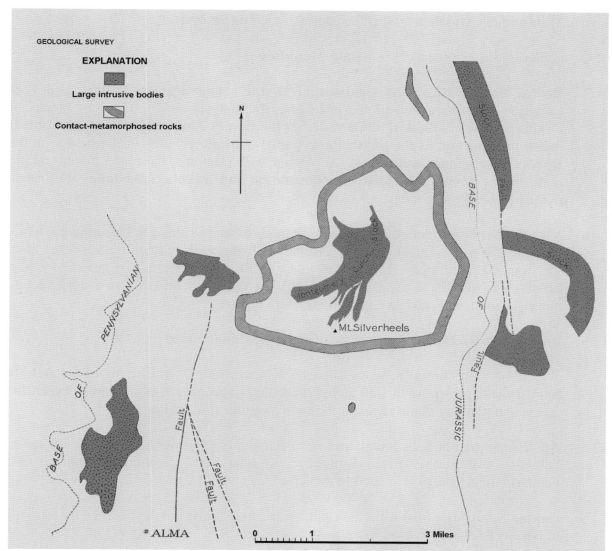

GEOLOGICAL SURVEY

EXPLANATION

Large intrusive bodies

Contact-metamorphosed rocks

Boreas Figure 7. Generalized map of Beaver-Tarryall area showing outlines of larger intrusive bodies and area of metamorphosed rocks (from Singewald, 1942).

6.4   Old settlement of Bentway. **Mount Silverheels** is at 10:00.

6.45   **Rocky Point.** Good opportunity to stretch one's legs. At the point a small section of the original railroad remains unaltered. From the point Tarryall Creek and Montgomery Gulch can be been to the west. Old workings of the Fortune Placer are visible to the left (Boreas Figure 6). Ditch routes to the Fortune and other placers can be traced.

7.4   **Boreas Mountain** (13,082 feet) is straight ahead. Left skyline is called **Hoosier Ridge** and is along the **Continental Divide.**

7.45   Road to left is to the Selkirk Campground, which is on the valley floor.

9.3   **Montgomery Gulch** at 9:00 is the center of the mineralized area.

10.6   High ridge at 12:00 and 2:00 is **Bald Mountain**.

11.5   **Boreas Pass** (11482 feet) **Continental Divide.   Leaving South Park** and Park County.   The foundation of the abandoned building on left is made of blocks of Dakota Sandstone. **Benton Shale** underlies the Boreas Pass, which is in **fault contact** (north continuation of the **South Park Fault**) immediately east of the pass with the **Boreas quartz monzonite stock.**   A syncline with Benton at the center trends straight north from the pass.   The **Morrison Formation and Dakota Sandstones** are present in the hillside west of the pass.

       Visit the Depot Restaurant in Como for pictures of trains caught in blizzards, etc while crossing this pass.   The building east of the road was recently rebuilt to show the hotel for stranded passengers.   From 1886 to 1906, Boreas Station at the pass had a post office (that was the highest in the country), a telegraph office, a two-story section house, a storehouse, and an engine house with turntable.

11.6   Road cuts in Cretaceous black shale, which is locally intruded by sills.

12.5   We are now on Summit County Road 10.   Greenish block weathering of the **Dakota Sandstone** is present to the left across the valley.   Straight ahead is **Mount Argentine** that is underlain by Pennsylvanian-Permian **Maroon Formation.**

12.8   An abandoned building foundation is to the right.   This was a train station called Farnham that served nearby mines.   A road sign pointing to Indiana and Pennsylvanian Creeks is located to the left.

12.9   **Dakota Sandstone** float is on the right.   Numerous **faults** cut the bedrock on this side of Boreas Pass.

13.2   Outcrops of **Maroon Formation**.   Note red roadbed.

13.7   Sign pointing to **Quandary Peak** (14,265 feet) is at 9:00.

14.3   At 11:00, Maroon Mountain.

14.8   Baker's Tank.   Still in **Maroon redbeds**.   The tank is located along a stream and was fed by gravity.   This tanks held 9,305 gallons.

15.3   **Mount Quandary** at 11:00.   The road is cut in the **Maroon Formation**.   Note **conglomerate**.

15.6   **Tertiary quartz monzonite dike** in **redbeds**.

15.7   Road bed changes from red to black in color.

15.9   Sliver of **Dakota Sandstone** in road cut.

16.2   **Quartz monzonite** exposures.

16.3   Low in valley to left is **Goose Pasture Tarn**, which is dammed to provide boating, etc. Note that dam fills a **natural breach in a terminal moraine** of the **Blue Valley glacier**.

16.6   **Quartz monzonite** is on right.

16.9   Sills in Cretaceous shale.

17.2   Excellent view of the **Tenmile Range**, which is cored with Precambrian metamorphics and flanked on the east by east-dipping Lower Paleozoic sediments. Numerous cirques, arêtes, and horns are visible.

17.3   Paved road.

17.4   **Stop. Dakota Sandstone** section. Look for dinosaur footprints.

17.5   **Benton Shale** in road cut.

19.3   Abundant **Dakota Sandstone** float on right.

19.6   Road sign "5 miles to Breckenridge". Bear left at the junction.

20.4   Exposures of **Benton Shale** are present to the left of the road.

21.4   Junction with Colorado 9 at south end of Breckenridge.

End of Road Log.

Boreas Figure 8. Close-up of welded debris flow in Como Hill.

Elkhorn Road Log
County Road 15
From US Highway 24 north to US Highway 285

Mileage
From US 24 (mileages are
<u>adjusted to posted mileage</u>)

0.0   Junction of US Highway 24 and Elkhorn Road (County Road 15). Turn north.
       Road is on upper part of Pierre Shale. Sandstone in cliff at 11:00 is South Park
       Formation.   D. L. Sawatsky (1972) labeled them Td=Tertiary Denver
       Formation.) Please see Sawatsky's Cross-section B-B' on US Highway 24
       Road Log Figure 8.

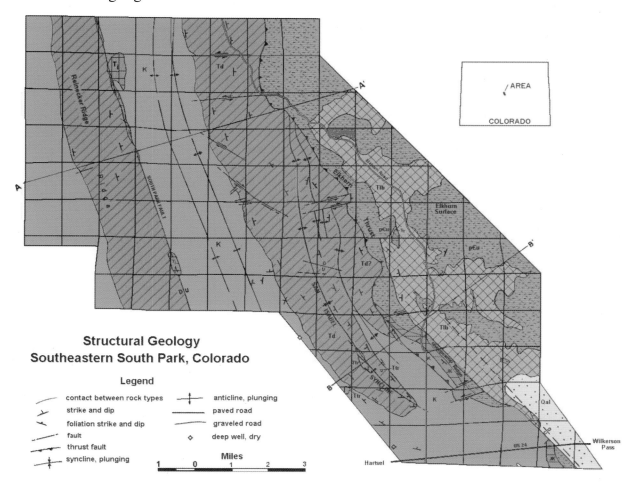

Structural Geology
Southeastern South Park, Colorado

Legend

contact between rock types	anticline, plunging
strike and dip	paved road
foliation strike and dip	graveled road
fault	deep well, dry
thrust fault	
syncline, plunging	

Miles

Elkhorn Figure 1. Geologic map of the south half of Elkhorn Road. From D. L. Sawatsky, 1972.
Please see US Highway 24 Road Log for an explanation of formation symbols on US 24 Figure 7 and
the cross sections posted on US 24 Figure 8.

0.9   Approximate south edge of Oligocene lake beds (Tlb) that unconformably overlie all older units.   The ridge at middle distance is Sheepcamp Ridge. The leading edge of the Elkhorn Overthrust is in the near slope of that ridge. High hills at 2:00 are Puma Hills of the west edge of the Front Range.

1.2   Scattered homes of the San Isabel community on left.

1.7   Sheepcamp Ridge at 12:00 to 3:00 has granites of the 1,700 m.y. age group thrust over Pierre Shale according to D. L. Sawatsky. Please see US Highway 24 Road Log Figure 8, Cross Section B-B'. Please also see the discussion of the Elkhorn Thrust in the Geologic History chapter (Tertiary Sediments) of this book. This is the leading edge of a 3.4 miles uplift of this part of the Front Range. The west flank of this range rode westward along a shallow ramp about five miles to this point. In other words, the west flank of the uplift rotated westward over the basin. This type of basin-ward rotation of uplifted areas is common to many uplifts of the Rocky Mountains (examples: Wind River Mountains southwestward over the Green River Basin; southern part of the Big Horn Mountain and the Casper Arch south and southwestward over the Wind River Basin; and the east side of the Front Range eastward over the Denver Basin.)

2.3   At 11:00. The contact of northeast dipping South Park beds with overthrust Precambrian granite is not clear.   At this point the road is on Oligocene lakebeds.

3.0   The thin-bedded limestone in the road cut is part of the lakebeds.

3.1   On right 100 feet north of the first tree the thin bedded and massive sandstones are mapped as steeply northeast dipping Dakota Sandstones immediately above the leading edge of the Elkhorn Overthrust.

Elkhorn Figure 2. MP 3.1. Exposures of soft Dakota Sandstones east of road. These outcrops are close to the eroded leading edge of the Elkhorn Thrust.

3.3   Settele Drive to right is along the crest of Sheepcamp Ridge and has excellent exposures of Precambrian igneous and metamorphic rocks. Jefferson Drive to left.

3.4   Precambrian metamorphic rocks in road cuts. These rocks are older than 1,700 m.y.

3.5   Oxford Road to right. The valley ahead is cut in lakebeds. Some maps show normal faults on both sides of this valley. It appears that the lake deposited sediments in a valley between thrust fronts.

4.2   Light-colored quartz-rich granite is exposed in the hills to the east and west. Puma Hills at 2:00.

4.3   Goldburg Canyon Road to right. Yellow ranch house on right.

4.6   Apache Trail to right.

4.7   Park to right. Precambrian rocks in near hills at 1:00.

4.9   Thin-bedded limestone (lakebeds) in road cuts.

5.1   Wildwood Recreational Village to right.

5.5   Lakebeds in road cuts.

6.5   Windmill on right.

7.2   Road is on lakebeds.

8.2   Cattle guard. Antelope Lane to right.

8.6   At 3:00. Outcrop capping hill is a course grained conglomeratic cross-bedded sandstone. On north side of this hill there is an outcrop of thin-bedded white limestone typical of Oligocene Lake beds. No fossils were found.

9.0   White layers in road cuts are thin-bedded limestones (lakebeds).

9.2   Log house on right.

9.3   Algal limestone in road cut. This outcrop is near the north edge of the lakebeds. Granite caps the hill.

9.4   Black schist in road cut.

9.8   Granite on hilltop to right.

10.4   Cattle guard.

11.8   CR 17 to left.

11.9   Just west of the road is the McMurry Oil Company 1-17 Tarryall Federal well, SW NE NE Section 17, Township 10 South, Range 75 West. The well has multiple valve completion head ("Christmas Tree") installed. This well was plugged and abandoned after being drilled to 12,768 feet by Hunt Oil Company in 1992. It was reentered and McMurry Oil Company set 5-½ inch casing to 11,360 feet in 1999. It is rumored to be a discovery well for a gas field.

In the original well the base of the Elkhorn Overthrust was picked at 1,900 feet (drilling depth) and the top of the Cretaceous at 5,270 feet. Dakota Formation (?) sands were tested at 10,200 to 10,275 feet (test did not work).

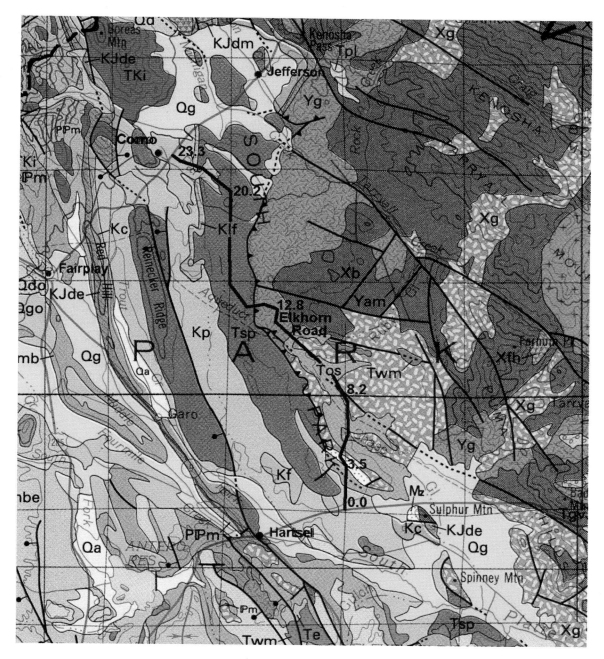

Elkhorn Figure 3. Geologic Map of entire Elkhorn Road. Please see Geologic History Figure 1 for an explanation of symbols.

12.1   Remington Road to right. Granitic rocks that crop out in this area are of the 1,400 m.y. age group.

12.3   At 4:00 to 5:00 the leading edge of Elkhorn thrust is covered by aspen in the middle of the slope.

Elkhorn Figure 4. MP 12.3. Looking east. Layer of aspens covers surface trace of Elkhorn Thrust. South Park Formation beds underlie slope in foreground. Scattered rock outcrops along pine-covered ridge are Precambrian granites.

Elkhorn Figure 5. Aerial view looking east at the northwest edge of the Elkhorn Overthrust. East-dipping, grass covered South Park Formation beds are in the foreground. Overthrust Precambrian granites and metamorphic rocks underlie the pine and aspen-covered terrain.

12.5   Reinecker Ridge at 11:00, Mount Silverheels at 12:00, and Boreas Mountain at 1:00. Road is now on east dipping South Park Formation outcrops.

13.8   Road cuts to left expose extrusive igneous rocks. Most are welded tuffs (ignimbrites) of Paleocene age (Zortman, et al, 1995). The source was probably an early stage of extrusives from the Boreas Stock.

13.9   Goshawk Road to left.

14.1   Ridge at 10:00 in near distance is the east dipping hogback of the Fox Hills Sandstone.

14.7   East dipping South Park Formation extrusive igneous rocks crop out in hill to right.

14.8   Road to Reinecker Ridge Elk Hunting Parking Area to left.

15.3   Boreas Mountain at 11:00 is near the middle of the very large Boreas stock Radioactive dates of 40 to 44 m.y. have been obtained thus far. The volcano over this stock was probably active and a major contributor during most of South Park Formation deposition.

16.6   Cattle guard.

16.9   Antler Ridge Road to right. Hills at 3:00 are leading edge of the Elkhorn Overthrust. High mountains to east are the Kenosha Mountains.

18.4   Cattle Guard. Road is now on the Como erosional and depositional surface.

18.7   Tarryall Creek.

19.0   Cattle guard. Back on Como surface. Indian Mountain Ranch at 9:00.

19.8   CR 32 to right. Jefferson-Como Fire Protection District 5 station on right. On Como surface.

20.3   King Mine is one mile southwest. The three coal beds that were mined are near the base of the Laramie Formation (above Fox Hills Sandstone). The mines had a reputation for being gassy and dangerous. One story says 16 men died in one accident.

Elkhorn Figure 6. Several piles of slag and the foundations of buildings are all that is left of the King Mine. In the hillside to the left (east) there are numerous areas of depression over collapsed tunnels.

22.6   Ridge at 10:30 is Como Hill.

23.3   Cattle guard and US Highway 285.

End of road log.

Guffey to Florissant Road Log
Guffey to Florissant along Park County Road 102
and Teller County Roads 112, 11 and 1

Part of log from Road Log by Epis, et al, 1976
Please see figures and discussion in Thirtynine Mile Volcanic Field
part of the Geologic History Chapter for the regional setting.

Cumulative Mileage	County Road 102 Mileage	
0.0	0.0	**Junction Colorado 9 and County Road 102.** Go north at Y on CR 102. Road cuts in Precambrian gneiss. Junction is at the **northeast edge of the Thirtyone Mile center** and one-half mile northwest of the **south edge of the Guffey Caldera** (please see Geologic History Figure 10). There is a **shear zone** along the **Current Creek Fault** (approximately along Colorado 9 north and south of this point) as the result of pre- and post-volcanic displacement on the fault.
0.3	0.3	On left, prospect in **Precambrian gneiss**. Probably looking for gold.
1.1	1.1	Entering **Guffey**. The town is near the center of the **Guffey Volcano** of the **Thirtynine Mile Volcanic Field**. There was extrusive activity in this field from 38 to 28 m.y. ago. The name Thirtynine Mile Volcanic Field is applied to a large area that includes four successive volcanic centers. Please see the Geologic History discussion. Also read *Cenozoic Volcanism in the Southern Rocky Mountains* edited by R, C. Epis, Colorado School of Mines Quarterly, Vol. 63, No. 3, July 1968.

The Guffey center of volcanism was the third and most prominent. The height of the Guffey Volcano is speculative (cover), but was probably greater than 6,000 feet above the South Park plain prior to collapse of the caldera. Note that this was at a time when the Florissant Lake beds were estimated to be 3,000 feet above sea level. The volcanic pile was high enough that mudflows extended 30 to 50 miles in some directions. Mudflows from the Guffey Volcano dammed the pre-Oligocene south-flowing drainage and caused a large lake to develop over South Park and in the Florissant Valley. The outlet from the South Park Lake became the South Platte River, which is superimposed across the Front Range.

The town of Guffey developed in 1894 when disgruntled miners left Cripple Creek in search of gold. Then known as "Freshwater", Guffey became a center of prospecting activity. The name changed when a senator from Pennsylvania offered the city fathers $500 to rename the town after him. Little gold was found, but the area has prospered because of ranching and timber. .

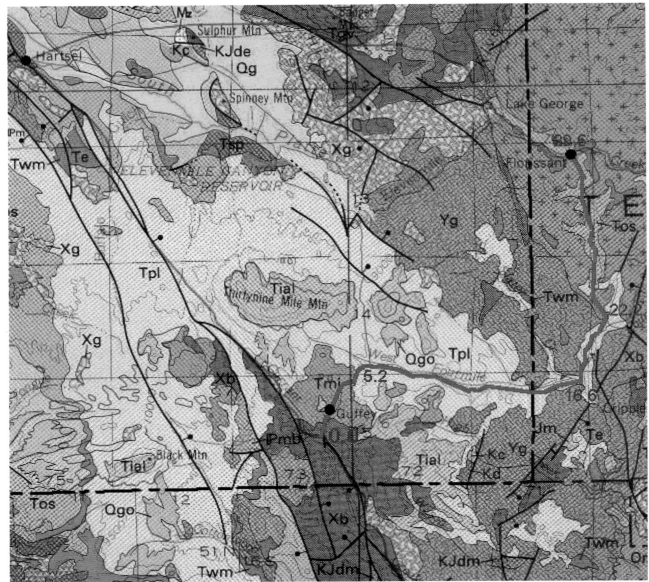

Guffey Figure 1. Geologic map with route of road log. From Tweto, 1979.
Please see Geologic History Figure 1 for an explanation of symbols.

Cumulative Mileage	County Road 102 Mileage	
1.7	1.7	**Precambrian granite** in road cut on left. The volcanic pile is built on eroded Precambrian rocks.
1.9	1.9	**CR122** to right. **Cover Mountain** (10,157 feet) at 3:00 is a **stock** of andesite and rhyolite rocks along the **southeast side of the Guffey caldera**. This stock was the source of early extrusions of the Guffey Center.

Box 2. The Sequence Of Events Associated With The Thirtynine Mile Volcanic Field Extrusive Centers Are Listed From Youngest To Oldest.

Fear Creek Conglomerate with Fish Creek Tuff (27.83 m.y.) from San Juan Volcanic Field

Upper Andesite: This is the youngest extrusive formation of the Thirtynine Mile field. It forms high slopes of **Waugh Mountain** above 9,800 feet. Basalt and andesite flows and flow breccias with minor tuffs. It probably came from fissures in the Waugh Mountains and is 300 to 1,200 feet thick in that area.

Waugh Mountain Center: Several domes, necks and dikes of latitic to rhyolitic composition lie along pre-volcanic faults

Ash Flow 7: Includes five flows that give a bench-like topography west of Waugh Mountain.

Ash Flow 6: Gribbles Park Tuff (32.9 m.y.)

Ash Flow 5, Antero Formation and Lake Florissant: Antero Formation has a Upper Course Sandstone and Conglomerate Member (1,300 feet) and a Lower Tuff and Limestone Member (2,000 feet, 33.65 to 33.71 m.y.)

Ash Flow 4: Agate Creek Tuff

Guffey Center of Thirtynine Mile Volcanic Field

Upper Andesite laharic breccia member: This unit has well-stratified andesitic to basaltic lava flows, laharic breccias and minor ash-fall tuffs. Mudflow rocks predominate and dip four to ten degrees away from Guffey Center. The unit is 2,000 feet thick on Thirtynine Mile Mountain. These rocks represent erosional flanks of a large composite volcano (Guffey Volcano). Basal diameters were 10 miles north-south and 16 miles east west. The dimensions of this volcano are of the same order as those of the large volcanic cones of the Middle Cascade Mountain in Oregon and Washington (Epis and Chapin, 1968). Collapse of the caldera probably occurred (possibly more than once) during extrusion of the Upper Andesite Member. There are several intrusive necks or stocks six miles west of Guffey along the southwest and west side of the collapse ring, including Hammond Peak, Baldy Mountain and Gold Hill. Epis and Chapin, 1968, identify these conduits as major feeds in the building of the Guffey Volcano.

Lower Andesite (34.1 m.y.): Numerous small vents around field erupted intermediate laharic breccias up to 500 feet thick that covers 800 square miles. **Ash flow 3** remnants are present in the lower 200 feet.

Thirtyone Mile Center: This 1,200-foot hornblende andesite dome tilts flows from Antelope Center and intrudes basic to intermediate flows, tuffs and breccias derived from that center. Thirtyone Mile center covers 8 to 10 square miles.

West Antelope Mountain Center: This is an 800-foot high lava dome with extrusive ash, pumice and tuff that covers three square miles.

Tallahassee Creek Conglomerate: Arkose plus fragments of Wall Mountain Tuff.

Stirrup Ranch Tuff (36.67 m.y.)

Wall Mountain Tuff (36.73 m.y.)

Prevolcanic Arkose: Balfour Formation of DeVoto, 1971. **Valley-fill in Late Eocene surface**.

Cumulative Mileage	County Road 102 Mileage	
2.3	2.3	Light colored rock on left is **Precambrian pegmatite** intruded into a shear zone.
2.7	2.7	Exposures of **granite**.
3.1	3.1	Exposures of **volcanics**.
3.3	3.3	**Volcanics. Ash, mudflow and lava. Cover Mountain** is at 1:00.
3.5	3.5	**Pikes Peak** at 12:00 beyond **McIntyre Mountain**.
3.8	3.8	**Andesite Lava** on left on road cut.
4.5	4.5	**CR 104** to right
5.2	5.2	**CR 59** to left. This junction is near the northeast edge of the caldera. The bedrock here is the **Lower Andesite**, lower member. There are a number of **basalt dikes** in this area. CR 59 goes north across the saddle between **Saddle Mountain** (10,801 feet) and **Thirtynine Mile Mountain** (11,433 feet). The later is north of the caldera and is composed of 3,000 feet of **mudflows and ignimbrites** with north dip. **Saddle Mountain** has the **northeast dip** of that

Guffey Figure 2. Outcrop of mud flow breccia near CR 59 at saddle between Thirtynine Mile Mountain and Saddle Mountain.

Guffey Figure 3. Same location. Outcrop of ignimbrite (welded tuff). Section is near vertical because of local faulting. Bright yellow-green is lichen growing on rock. The ignimbrite is a pinkish-gray.

Cumulative Mileage	County Road 102 Mileage	
		flank of the volcano. Farther north CR 59 goes by both Elevenmile Canyon and Spinney Mountain reservoirs
5.4	5.4	**Saddle Mountain** at 9:00. **Witcher Mountain** at 10:30. **McIntyre Mountain** at 11:00.
6.4	6.4	**Witcher Mountain** (9,994 feet) at 1:30. **East dipping mud flows** of the **Lower Andesite**, upper member (dated at 34.1 m.y.).
6.8	6.8	**Castle Mountain** (10,066 feet) at 9:00, **McIntyre Mountain** (9,672 feet) at 12:00. Both are capped by **east dipping** (two to six degrees) **mudflows** of the **Lower Andesite**, upper member. Note that the volcano was asymmetric, probably because of prevailing winds. Here the **east flank dips are two to six degrees**. North flank dips on Thirtynine Mile Mountain are 10 to 15 degrees. West flank dips at Black Mountain are eight degrees. Road is along **Fourmile Creek**.
7.1	7.1	**Dark rounded outcrops** north of Fourmile Creek are **mud flows**. They probably filled **small valleys** at time of deposition.

8.7   8.7   Good view of **low angle east dip** in ledges of **Castle Mountain** at 9:00.

Guffey Figure 4. Saddle Mountain from south. Dip of flows is to the northeast.

9.6   9.6   **McIntyre Mountain** at 9:00. Multiple layers of mudflows and ash.

Cumulative Mileage	County Road 102 Mileage	
11.1	11.1	Road cut in **mudflow.**
11.8	11.8	**Mudflow** at 9:00.
12.1	12.1	Road cut in **mudflow**. Mudflows also are exposed north of Fourmile Creek.
12.7	12.7	**CR 71** to left.

Guffey Figure 5. McIntyre Butte from south. In middle slope mudflow deposits dip to east.

Cumulative Mileage	Teller CR 112 Mileage	
14.3	0.0	**CR 112** at **Teller County** line.
15.0	0.7	There is a mound of mud flow material near the creek. The hills on either side of the creek are Pikes Peak granite (1.0 b.y.).

Cumulative Mileage	Teller CR 11 Mileage	
16.6	6.6	Junction with **CR 11**, turn left.
16.7	6.7	Cross **West Fourmile Creek**.

Cumulative Mileage	Teller CR 11 Mileage	
17.2	6.8	**Mt. Pisgah** at 3:00. Crossing terrace alluvium. Mt. Pisgah is a **phonolite plug** on the west side of the **Cripple Creek Volcanic Center.** Please read A. H. Koschmann (1949) for a description of the Cripple Creek gold field.
17.7	7.6	Good outcrops of **Tallahassee Creek Conglomerate** on right (see Box 2).

17.9   7.9   **Contact of andesite breccias** of lower member of the Thirtynine Mile Andesite with the **older Tallahassee Creek Conglomerate**. The conglomerate consists of clasts of porphyritic volcanic rock, dense quartzite and Wall Mountain Tuff. It occupies valleys that were entrenched into the late Eocene surface **after** deposition of the Wall Mountain Tuff in early Oligocene time.

18.4   8.4   Fourmile Fire House sets on **Pikes Peak Granite.**

20.0   8.7   **Wright Reservoir** at 3:00. Exhumed **late Eocene surface** is visible atop low hills of **Cripple Creek Quartz Monzonite** on left (west). To the east (right) the same surface is **faulted up** to the level of Cripple Creek townsite along the **Oil Creek fault** zone. The fault scarp generally bounds the east side of Fourmile Creek for many miles to the south.

20.5   9.7   **Contact** of **Pikes Peak Granite** and **Cripple Creek Monzonite** buried beneath alluvium and andesite breccias. There is a rounded outcrop of Pikes Peak granite at 12:00 to 1:00.

Cumulative Mileage	Teller CR 1 Mileage	

22.2   8.6   **Evergreen Station,** Junction with **CR 1**, turn left. Along the creek east of the junction, mudflows from the Guffey Volcano lie **on Pikes Peak granite**.

24.4   9.8   **Pikes Peak Granite** in hills to right.

29.0   13.2   Crossing **mudflow breccias** that filled a **south flowing Late Eocene valley** and formed a **dam,** behind which **Lake Florissant** extended approximately 12 miles north and northwestward to the vicinity of the town of Lake George. The famous Florissant Lake sediments accumulated in this lake.

26.4   14.4   **CR 42** to right. **Lake sediments** crop out in road cuts along this road. Petrified wood is fairly common.

27.3   15.3   Entrance **Florissant Fossil Beds National Monument** to left. Visitor Center is at 8,400 feet. Congress authorized the formation of the Florissant Fossil Beds National Monument on August 20, 1969. The action was prompted by concern over rapidly expanding real estate subdivisions within the Florissant area. The national monument consists of 6,000 acres south of the town of Florissant.

Cumulative Teller
Mileage   CR 1 Mileage

The **Florissant lake deposits** consist dominantly of **volcanic detritus** and are less than 150 feet thick. Tuffaceous shales and mudstones near the middle of the sequence contain most of the delicately preserved fossil plant and insect remains. Andesite tuffs and mudflows underlying them preserve petrified stumps and logs of giant Sequoia trees. Judging from the nature of the sediments and fauna, MacGinitie (1953) concluded that ancient Lake Florissant existed under climatic conditions that were warm, perhaps subtropical at an elevation of 3,000 feet. (His elevation is not accepted by all). Radioactive age determinations by the USGS indicate the lake existed during the early Oligocene, about 34 m.y. ago.

27.6   15.6   **Seguoia stumps** can be seen at 9:00 just below tree line.

28.2   16.2   **Homestead** on left.

29.4   17.4   **Florissant**.

29.6   17.6   Junction US Highway 24, end of road log.

Guffey Figure 6. Sequoia stump at Florissant National Monument.

Guffey Figure 7. Florissant lake deposits near the townsite of Florissant.

Park County Roads 53, 84 and 86 and
Chaffee County Road 187 Road Log
From 1 ½ miles south of Hartsel southwest to Park County line and
northwest in Chaffee County along CR 187 to U.S. 285

Data from Geology of the Antero Quadrangle by R. H. DeVoto
Colorado School of Mines Quarterly, Vol.66, No 3, 1971

Mileage
from Col 9

0.0   **Junction of Colorado 9 and County Road (CR) 53**, one and one half miles southeast of Hartsel. The road is on the **Balfour Formation** of DeVoto, 1971. Other geologists have mapped this section as **South Park (also called Denver) Formation**. The section is up to 400 feet of tuffaceous, volcanic sandstones and tuffs. It is hard to tell the two sections apart, but based on the lack of Laramide dip and conformable relation to the overlying Wall Mountain Tuff, DeVoto concluded that the Balfour Formation was early Oligocene in age as compared with the Paleocene-Eocene South Park (Denver) Formation.

County Road 53 follows the Ute Trail, which was used by Indians crossing the Park from Kenosha or Wilkerson Passes as one of the major routes through the Rockies (McConnell, 1966)

0.7   Road crosses a **small northwest trending horst block**. **Precambrian** biotite **quartz monzonite** is exposed in the hill. Faulting predates deposition of the Balfour Formation.

1.0   **Southwest side of horst**. Balfour Formation.

2.4   **Lower Volcanic Conglomerate** here overlies Balfour Formation. The hill at 3:00 is another partially buried northwest trending **horst block** with **Precambrian monzonite** exposed. Hill at 9:00 is **Wall Mountain Tuff**. To clarify stratigraphic relationships, in addition to CR 53 Figure 2, please also see Box 2 of Guffey Road Log.

3.6   **Crossing buried fault** at southwest side of second horst block.

4.2   **Thirtynine Mile volcanic field deposits**. **Lower andesite flows** are overlain by **mudflow breccias** (laharic breccia).

5.1   Base of upper member of the **Lower volcanic conglomerate** is here represented by mudflows (andesite laharic breccia).

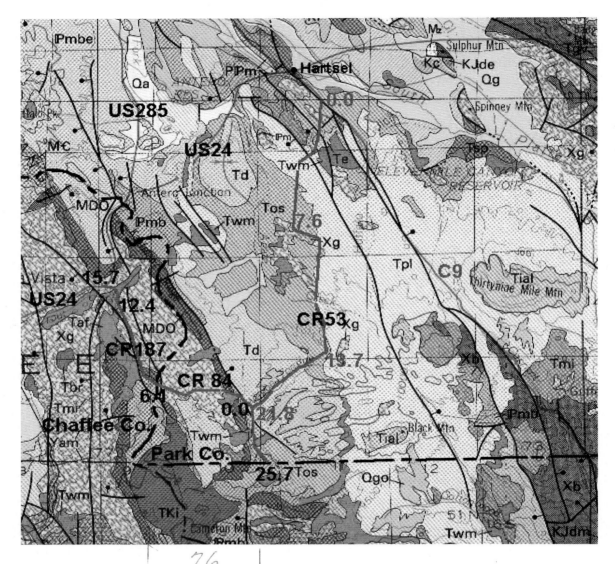

CR53 Figure 1. Geologic Map with route of road log (from Tweto, 1979). Please see Geologic History Figure 1 for an explanation of symbols.

5.2 **Road crosses buried fault**. Please see Cross sections A-A' and B-B' on plate 1 of DeVoto, 1971. A slightly younger section of the lower volcanic conglomerate section is exposed here with a small lens of limestone.

5.5 **Contact with younger Antero Formation**. Note local lenses of lacustrine limestone (lake deposits) over the next one and one-half miles.

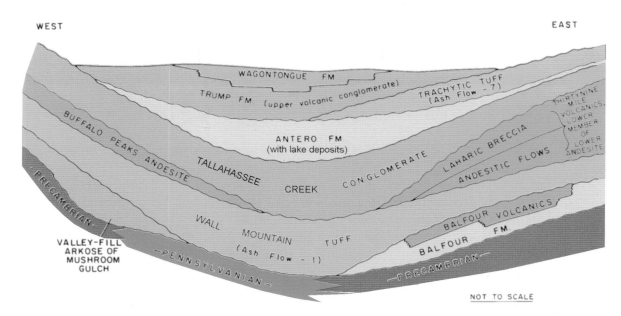

WEST   EAST

CR 53 Figure 2. Generalized sketch of stratigraphic relationships of Tertiary rocks, Antero Syncline area (after DeVoto, 1971).

CR53 Figure 3. At MP 4.2. Mudflow breccia (also called laharic breccia). Angular pieces of andesite lava with a mud (volcanic ash) matrix.

6.7   Poyner Ranch road is to the right. BM 9,118 feet here (BM = Bench Mark, which is an USGS surveyed elevation).

7.6   Road curves to southeast, hills at 3:00 are **Precambrian quartz monzonite**. Note that the Precambrian rocks are hills that were on-lapped by the Tertiary volcanics and lakes. An extensive limestone section surrounds the Precambrian hills at the contact between the Antero Formation and the Precambrian rocks. It appears to be a **beach facies of the Oligocene lake**.

8.7   Road crosses **limestone section** at the base of the Antero Formation.

9.3   **Mudflows** of upper member of lower andesite-lower member of Thirtynine Mile volcanic field.

9.6   **Contact of mudflows with the Antero Formation** on the south side of the hill. Hills at 3:00 are Precambrian schist and gneiss.

9.7   Road for next 2.0 miles is parallel to the **contact between the mudflows** and the **Antero Formation**.

10.6   Cattleguard.

10.8   Outcrop of **Precambrian quartz monzonite** to right surrounded by beach facies of Antero Lake beds.

11.7   Road curves to southeast.

12.0   **Precambrian rocks** in hill to right.

12.7   **Contact between Antero Formation and mudflows**.

12.9   **Thin bedded limestone** in ditch to right. Ostracod carapaces are common. (The exoskeleton of this water flea is less that 1 mm in diameter. Like all arthropods (insects) this animal periodically sheds its exoskeleton, which looks like a very small ladybug shell. Thus the shells are abundant and often look like a large sand grains in the white limestone.) Other fossils are present that look like impressions of larvae.

13.7   Road to left (east), continue on right fork. **Breccias** of the lower member of the Thirtynine Mile volcanic field are present on the northeast side of the road. There is a **welded tuff** in the road cut at the Y.

13.8   Agate Creek.

13.9   **Contact of mudflows** with overlying **Antero Formation.**

16.0   Cattleguard.

16.1   Road curves to southwest, crosses a divide, **leaves South Park**, and then continues along **Wagon Tongue Creek**.

CR53 Figure 4. At MP 13.7 Mud flow breccia.

18.0   Road to right. BM 9,497 feet. **Unconformity**. Miocene **Trump Formation** overlies Oligocene **Antero Formation**. Dip is to southwest into the **trough** of the **Antero syncline.** The lithology of the 300-foot +/- thick Trump Formation is dominated by white to buff conglomerates and white to buff sandstones. Sandy siltstones and mudstones may be present. Cut and fill channels and extreme lateral variability are characteristic of the Trump. Andesite pebbles predominate in the conglomerates.

18.5   Road to right. **Contact** of the 700-foot +/- thick **Wagontongue Formation** with the **Trump Formation**. The dip is still to the southwest. (Please see Cross section D-D' of DeVoto, 1971.) The Wagontongue is like the Trump, but with more mud and a predominance of Precambrian and Wall Mountain Tuff pebbles in the conglomerates.

18.9   Cattleguard.

20.0   Cattleguard. Approximate trough **of Antero syncline**.

20.8   **Trump Formation outcrops** on hillside.

21.8   **Junction with CR 84**. This road connects with CR 86 to Bassam Park, which is a downfaulted section of Paleozoic rocks in this part of the southern Mosquito Range. Chaffee CR 187 north from Bassam Park will take you back to US

Highway 285 east of Buena Vista. Badger Creek here parallels CR 53. Mountains to the right and off to the northwest are the Kaufman Ridge Uplift of the southern part of the Mosquito Range. The high ridge along the northeast side is composed of the more resistant, steeply east dipping (18 to 78 degrees) Lower Paleozoic quartzite and dolomite section.

22.5   Hills to right are **on** the **upthrown side of a fault.** The rocks are **Lower Paleozoic limestones**.

22.7   Cattleguard.

23.5   Outcrop on right is **Wall Mountain Tuff.**

23.8   West-dipping white hill to right is part of the **Antero Formation.** The rocks are probably **deposits of volcanic ash in a lake**.

24.1   Cattleguard.

24.7   **Terrace** along Badger Creek.

25.0   **Maroon red beds** are exposed in the hillside west of Badger Creek.

25.4   **Wall Mountain Tuff** crops out to left.

25.6   **Ford of Badger Creek**.

25.7   **County line:** entering Fremont County. CR 2 continues southwest through some spectacular country to Salida.

   Retrace route
to junction with CR 84
Cumulative Mileage

0.0   **Junction CR 53 and CR 84**. Head north on CR 84.

0.4   Cattleguard. Enter Badger Creek Ranch.

0.5   **Bridge** over **Badger Creek**.

1.5   Turn right on McMurry Road. Outcrop at 2:00 is **granite** of **Kaufman Ridge Uplift.**

1.8   **Volcanics** in road cut are an old valley fill. **Massive outcrops of granite** at 5:00 on north flank of Cals Fork Gulch.

2.9   Road to right, stay on McMurry Road.

3.1   Cattleguard. Enter San Isabel National Forest.

CR 53 Figure 5. At intersection of CR 86 with Chaffee CR 187. View is across Bassam Park. Sawatch Range is in the distance.

CR 53 Figure 6. Aerial view looking south at Bassam Park.

3.3   Cross creek.

3.5   **Precambrian granite** on left.

4.0   Turn right on CR 86.

5.4   Road crosses outcrop of **Wall Mountain Tuff**. Tuff is also exposed on the hillside to the right.

5.9   **Volcanics** in hills composed of welded tuff and ash.

6.1   Intersection with Chaffee CR 187. Maps show the county line through this point. Continue right on CR 187. **Black dumps** southeast of the intersection are piles of Belden Shale. DeVoto's map of the Antero Quadrangle shows the north-south **East Bassam fault** through this point. Precambrian gneiss is exposed on the upthrown east side and Pennsylvanian Belden Formation is present on the west side. Bassam Forest Service Campground is about one mile south.

6.5   Traveling north on CR 187 along **southwest side of Bassam Ridge** on the **northeast side of Bassam Park**. At this point, Bassam Park is a **south-southeast plunging syncline** with **Maroon Red Beds** in the trough and **Lower Paleozoic limestones** cropping out on either side.

7.2   **Lower Paleozoic limestones** in the hillside to the right.

7.5   **Lower Paleozoic limestone (Leadville Limestone)** in road cut.

8.4   Aspen Ridge Road to left, keep on CR 187.

8.8   Cattleguard.

9.9   Outcrop of **granite** on right.

10.2   Cattleguard. **Granite** outcrops.

10.5   CR 188 to right. Stay on CR 187.

11.3   **Wall Mountain Tuff** at 12:00.

11.7   Cattleguard.

11.9   **Precambrian pegmatite** in hillside on right.

12.4   Steeply northwest dipping beds of **Wall Mountain Tuff** on right is one of the **Castle Rocks**.

CR 53 Figure 7. At CR 187 MP 12.4. Very thick section of Wall Mountain Tuff. This ignimbrite outcrop is on the south side of a thick valley fill. Collapse of the center of the valley resulted in the Castles, the wall-like erosional remnants of the Wall Mountain Tuff on either side of the east-trending valley. Section is very thick because it is located near the source of the pyroclastic flow.

12.8   **Paleozoic beds on skyline** at 12:00 dip east on the **east flank** of **Kaufman Ridge**, which is a **southern continuation of the Mosquito Range.**

13.2   Crossing **tuff-filled valley.** At the time of deposition of the tuff this valley was east-flowing as part of the **Late Eocene Surface** on the **east flank of the giant Laramide Sawatch Anticline.**

13.8   **Wall Mountain Tuff** on north side of paleovalley. This peak combined with Castle Rock and other Wall Mountain Tuff peaks in this area are collectively called **The Castles.**

14.1   Trout Creek. Turn left on CR 309.

14.3   Wall of Wall **Mountain Tuff** at 11:00.

14.5   **Tuff** in road cut.

14.6   **Coarsely crystalline granite** in road cut.

15.0   **Coarsely crystalline granite.**

15.7   Railroad ranch on left: junction with US Highway 285.

End of Road Log.

CR 53 Figure 8. A view of two of the Castles. These Wall Mountain Tuff outcrops are part of the south flank of the valley. On rim at left skyline (part of Kaufman Ridge) are east-dipping limestones of the Lower Paleozoic section.

Selected References

1. Behre, C. H. Jr., 1953, Geology and Ore Deposits of the West Slope of the Mosquito Range: U. S. Geological Survey Professional Paper 235. (Covers Leadville Mining District).

2. Chapin, C.E. and S, A, Kelley, 1997, The Rocky Mountain Erosion Surface in the Front Range of Colorado: *in* Colorado Front Range Guidebook, Rocky Mountain Association of Geologists.

3. Chronic, Halka, 1980, Roadside Geology of Colorado: Mountain Press Pub. Co., Missoula, Montana, 322 p.

4. Chronic, John, 1964, Geology of the Southern Mosquito Range, Colorado: The Mountain Geologist, Vol. 1, No 3, p.103-114.

5. Clement, J. H. and G. L. Dolton, 1970, A Chronicle of Exploration in South Park Basin, Park County, Colorado: The Mountain Geologist, vol.7, no.3, p.205-218.

6. Curtis, B. F., 1975, *editor,* Cenozoic History of Southern Rocky Mountains: Geol. Soc. America Memoir 144.

7. DeVoto, R. H., 1964, Stratigraphy and Structure of Southwestern South Park, Park County, Colorado: The Mountain Geologist, vol.1, No. 3, p.117-126.

8. " , 1971, Cenozoic Geologic History of South Park and Geology of the Antero Reservoir Quadrangle, Colorado: Quarterly of the Colorado School of Mines, V. 66, No. 3, 90 p., 2 plates.

9. " , 1972, Cenozoic Geologic History of South Park: The Mountain Geologist, vol. 9, no.2-3, p. 211-222.

10. " , 1980a, Mississippian Stratigraphy and History of Colorado: *in* Kent, H.C. and K. W. Porter, *editors*, Colorado Geology, Rocky Mountain Assoc. Geologist (RMAG) Guidebook.

11. " , 1980b, Pennsylvanian Stratigraphy and History of Colorado: *op cit.*

12. Epis, R. C., 1968, *editor*, Cenozoic Volcanism in the Southern Rocky Mountains: Quarterly of the Colorado School of Mines, Vol. 63, No. 3.

13. Epis, R. C. and C. E. Chapin, 1968, Geologic History of the Thirty-nine Mile Volcanic Field, Central Colorado: Colorado School of Mines Quarterly, vol. 63, no. 3, p. 51-86.

14.   "   , 1974, Stratigraphic nomenclature of the Thirtynine Mile volcanic field, central Colorado: U. S. Geological Survey Bull. 1395-C, p. C1-C23.

15. Epis, R.C., G. R. Scott, R. B. Taylor and C. E. Chapin, 1980, Summary of Cenozoic Geomorphic, Volcanic and tectonic Features in Central Colorado and adjoining areas: Rocky Mountain Association of Geologists Symposium, p. 135-156

16. Epis, R.C., G. R. Scott, R. B. Taylor and W. N. Sharp, 1976, *Road log,* Petrologic, Tectonic, and Geomorphic Features of Central Colorado: Studies in Field Geology, Colorado School of Mines, no. 8, Nov. p.301-321.

17. Gerhard, L. C. , R. B. Chase and J. H. Lewis, 1970, Second Day's Road Log, Canon City, Fairplay and Breckenridge: The Mountain Geologist, V. 7, No. 3, P.229-242.

18. Graebner, Peter and R. C. Epis, Remnant Magnetism in Major Rock Units of the Thirty-nine Mile Volcanic Field-Abstract, p. 87-88.

19. Hutchinson, R.M., 1976, Granite Tectonics of Pikes Peak Batholith: Colorado School Of Mines Studies in Field Geology No. 8, p. 32-43.

20. Kelley, S. A. and C. E. Chapin, 1997, Internal Structure of the Southern Front Range, Colorado, From an Apatite Fission-Track Thermochronology Perspective: *in* Colorado Front Range Guidebook, Rocky Mountain Assoc. Geologist, p.19-30.

21. Kent, H. C., *et al,* 1972, Guidebook, Energy and Mineral Resources of the Southern Rocky Mountains: The Mountain Geologist, Vol. 9, no.2-3

22.   "   , 1972, Road Log Buena Vista to Cripple Creek, p 189-206

23. Koschmann, A. H. 1949, Structural Control of the Gold Deposits of the Cripple Creek District, Teller Creek, Colorado: U. S. Geological Survey Bull 955-B, 60 pages.

24. LeRoy, L. W., 1964 Generalized Composite Geological Sections, South Park, Colorado: The Mountain Geologist, Vol. 1, No. 3, p.115.

25. MacGinitie, H. D., 1953, Fossil Plants of the Florissant Beds, Colorado: Carnegie Inst. Washington Pub.599, Contr. Paleontology, 198 p.

26. Malan, R. C., 1969, Uranium in the Tertiary Intermontane Basins of Colorado: The Mountain Geologist, Vol. 6, no.1, p. 41-52.

27. Mallory, W.W., 1972, Pennsylvanian Arkose and the Ancestral Rocky Mountains: *in* Mallory, W. W., *Editor,* Geologic Atlas of the Rocky Mountains Area; Rocky Mountain Assoc Geologists publication, p. 131-132.

28. McConnell, Virginia, 1966, Bayou Salado: Sage Books, Swallow Press, Chicago, Ill. 60605

29. McGookey, D. P., *et al,* 1972, Cretaceous System: *in* Mallory, W. W., *editor,* 1972, Geologic Atlas of the Rocky Mountain Area: Rocky Mountain Assoc. Geologists publication, p. 190-228.

30. Meierding, T. C. and P. W. Birkeland, 1980, Quaternary Glaciation of Colorado: Rocky Mountain Assoc. Geologists Symposium, p. 165-174.

31. Misantoni, Dean, M. L. Silberman and B. K. Lees, 1998, Geology of the Sweet Home Mine and Alma District: *in* The Sweet Home Mine, Mineralogy Record, v. 29, no.4.

32. Mohlenbrock, R.H., 1994, Hoosier Ridge, Colorado: Natural History, vol. 103, No. 9, p.70-72.

33. Mohlenbrock, R. H., 1995, High Creek Fen, Colorado: Natural History, Vol. 104 No. 6, p. 16-19.

34. Moore, Thomas, et al, 1998, The Sweet Home Mine: The Mineral Record, v. 29, no. 4 (P.O. Box 35565, Tucson, AR 85740).

35. Sanders, G. F., 1975, Geology of Buffalo Peaks: Colorado School of Mines Masters Thesis.

36. Sanders, G. F. ,Jr., G. R. Scott and C. W. Naeser, 1976, The Buffalo Peaks Andesite of Central Colorado: U. S. Geological Survey Bulletin 1405-F.

37. Sawatzky, D. L., 1972, Structural Geology of Southeastern South Park: The Mountain Geologist, vol. 9, no.2-3, p.223-226.

38. Singewald, Q. D., 1942, Stratigraphy, Structure and Mineralization in the Beaver-Tarryall Area, Park County, Colorado: U. S. Geological Survey Bulletin 928-A. 44 p., 5 plates.

39. " , 1950, Gold Placers and Their Geologic Environment in Northwestern Park County, Colorado: U. S. Geological Survey Bull 955-D, p. 103-172.

40. Singleton, Q,D., and B. S. Butler, 1941, Ore Deposits in the Vicinity of the London Fault of Colorado: U. S. Geological Survey Bulletin 911, 74 p. 21 plates.

41. Stark, J.T., et al, 1949, Geology and Origin of South Park, Colorado: Geol. Soc. America Memoir 33

42. Steven, T. A. and R. C. Epis, 1968, Oligocene Volcanism in South-Central Colorado: Quarterly of the Colorado School of Mines, v. 63, no. 3, p. 241-258.

43. Taylor, A. M., 1999, Guide to the Geology of Colorado: Cataract Lode Mining Company, 2108 Arapahoe St., Golden, Colorado, 222 pages.

44. Tweto, Ogden, 1980, Tectonic History of Colorado: Rocky Mountain Assoc. Geologists (RMAG) Symposium, p. 5-10.

45.   "   , 1980, Precambrian Geology of Colorado: RMAG Symposium, p. 37-46.

46.   "   , 1980, Summary of Laramide Orogeny in Colorado: RMAG Symposium, p.129-134.

47. Washburne, C.W., 1910, The South Park Coal Field, Colorado: U. S. Geological Survey Bull 381, p.307-316.

48. Weimer, R. J., 1970, Dakota Group (Cretaceous) Stratigraphy, Southern Front Range, South and Middle Parks, Colorado: The Mountain Geologist, Vol. 7, No. 3, p.157-184.

49. Wobus, R. A., 1976, New Data on Potassic and Sodic Plutons of the Pikes Peak Batholith, Central Colorado: Colorado School of Mines Studies in Colorado Field Geology, No. 8, p. 57-67.

50. Yacoub, N. K., 1965, Magnetic Survey of the Jefferson Area: The Mountain Geologist, vol.2, No. 4, p.193-201.

51. Zortman, R.E., C. A. Bush and Carl Abston, 1995, National Geochronological and Natural Radioelement Data Bases: U. S. Geological Survey Digital Data Series DDS-14.

Glossary

Alpine glacier Any glacier in a mountain range. It usually originates in a *cirque* and flows down into a valley.

Andesite See *Igneous Rocks*

Anticline Where rock layers (beds) are arched up (up-folded) so the beds on the two sides of the fold are inclined (dip) away from each other along a common ridge or axis, similar to the two opposite slopes in the roof of a quonset hut. Opposite of *Syncline*, which is a down fold of bedded rocks.

Arete The sharp, jagged crest along the divide between two cirques that results from backward erosion of the walls of the adjoining cirques.

Arkose Sandstone with a high percentage of feldspar grains.

Ash flow An avalanche of volcanic ash, generally a highly heated mixture of volcanic gases and ash that travels down the flanks of a volcano or along the surface of the ground.

Ash-flow tuff Consolidated volcanic ash deposited from an ash flow.

Batholith A great irregular mass of intrusive igneous rock underlying or exposed over an area greater than 100 km^2. Batholiths originate as deep seated igneous rock masses (harden magma). Batholiths are sometimes enlarged or derived from surrounding rock through very high temperature and pressure metamorphism.

Bedding A characteristic of sedimentary rocks in which parallel planar surfaces separate layers of different grain sizes or composition deposited at different times.

Breccia A fragmental rock whose components are angular, thus distinguished from a conglomerate, which is composed of rounded pebbles, cobbles or boulders. Can include pebble to bounder-size angular rocks.

b.y. Billions of years before present.

Caldera A large basin-shaped volcanic depression that forms after a very large eruption when the volcano collapses through the roof of the emptied magma chamber.

Center (volcanic) Source area of an extrusive volcanic pile. May include one or many vents.

Central vent The main vent of a volcano, situated at the center of the cone.

Cenozoic Geologic era from 65 m.y. to Present. Periods are:

Period	Begins
Quaternary	1.8 m.y.
Tertiary	65 m.y.

Cirque   The head of a glacial valley with the form of an amphitheater. The upper edges have the steepest slopes, approaching the vertical, and the base may be flat or hollowed out. A small lake commonly occupies the base after deglaciation.

Colorado Mineral Belt. Linear geographic area extending from the Telluride area of southwest Colorado, northeast to the Boulder area. This belt contain most of the metal mines in Colorado. This area was mineralized by *hydrothermal* solutions during intrusive and extrusive episodes of the Cretaceous and Tertiary.

Diatreme   A volcanic vent filled with volcanic breccia. Formed by the explosive escape of gases.

Dike   A tabular igneous intrusion that cuts across structures of surrounding rock.

Dip   The angle by which bedding of sedimentary or extrusive rocks deviates from the horizontal. The angle is measures in a plane perpendicular to the *strike*.

Dome (tectonic)   A round or elliptical anticlinal upwarp in which the strata dip away in all directions from a high point.

Eolian   Pertaining to or deposited by wind.

Epirogeny   Large scale, regional, primarily vertical movement of the earth's crust.

Erratic   Rock fragment (usually boulder size) carried by a glacier away from the outcrop from which it was derived.

Extrusive   The venting of molten rocks at the surface. May be by flow (lava) or explosion (ash, volcanic bombs) depending on amount of gas in the magma. May be from fissures (fractures or joints) or from volcanic vents. Opposite to *intrusive*.

Fault   A planar fracture in the earth's crust across which there has been relative displacement of the two blocks parallel to the fracture. **Dip-slip or normal fault:** One side slips down the plane of the fault relative to the other. **Strike-slip fault**: One side slips lateral (horizontal) relative to the other. **Reverse fault**: One side is pushed up the plane of the fault relative to the other. Angle of the fault is usually greater than 45 degrees. **Thrust fault**: One side is pushed over the other. Angle of the fault will be less than 45 degrees and may be very shallow, even horizontal.

Fault block mountains A mountain or range formed when the crust is broken into blocks of different elevations by faulting.

Fold   Bent or warped bedding or sequence of beds that was originally horizontal, or nearly so, and was subsequently deformed.

Formation   The fundamental unit in rock stratigraphic classification. It is a set of rocks (1)that is or once was nearly continuous horizontally, (2)that shares some distinctive features of lithology, and (3)that is widespread and thick enough to be mapped.

Glaciation   The formation, movement, and recession of ice glaciers. Includes also the erosion caused by ice movement and the transport of rocks and mud in and on top of the ice. Glaciation is a major means of forming the landscapes of high altitude (above 10,000 feet) areas in the South Park Region.

Glacial Period During the last 1.6 million years there have been several periods during which glaciers formed above 11,000 feet and move down valleys to altitudes of above 10,000 feet. Glacial periods are characterized by higher rates of precipitation, erosion and transport and deposition of sediment in valleys below 10,000 feet.

Glass (volcanic) A rock formed when magma or molten rock is cooled too rapidly to allow crystal growth. May form the matrix of an ignimbrite (welded tuff). Obsidian is a volcanic glass.

Group   A series of two or more formations.

Hanging valley Valley left by a melted glacier tributary that entered a larger valley above its base, high up on the valley wall.

Hogback   A ridge formed by the slower erosion of steeply dipping hard strata.

Horn   Three or four sided peak with glacial erosion on all sides. (Matterhorn Peak in the Alps is the model)

Hydrothermal Literally, hot water. Mineral deposits are carried upward from magmas by hot gaseous waters and the minerals are deposited when the gas is released and/or the water cools.

Igneous rocks
         `Acidic   **Intermediate**   **Basic**

Extrusive and fine-grained intrusive rocks
rhyolite   trachyte   andesite   basalt

Intrusive - course grained rocks
granite   granodiorite   diorite   gabbro

Ignimbrite   See *Tuff, Welded Tuff.*

Intermontane Situated between or surrounded by mountains.

Intrusive   The forced emplacement of molten rock between layers of rock or along fractures or faults. Intrusive rocks solidify below the earth's surface. Opposite to *extrusive*.

Joint   Naturally occurring vertical or near vertical crack in rocks.

Laccolith   A concordant, intrusive body that has spread laterally between rock layers doming the overlying rocks but not deforming the underlying rocks. Thus a laccolith normally has a flat base and is mushroom-shaped.

Lahar   A *mudflow* of unconsolidated volcanic ash, dust, breccia and boulder, that occurs when pyroclastic deposits mix with rain or the water from a lake, stream or melting glacier and flow down the sides of a volcano, sometimes for many miles and with catastrophic effect.

m.y.   Age of rock in millions of years before present.

Magma   Molten rock that forms igneous rocks upon cooling.

Magma chamber Feeds magma to intrusive or extrusive emanations.

Mesozoic   Geologic era from 245 to 65 m.y. Geologic periods within this era

Periods	Begins
Cretaceous	146 m.y.
Jurassic	208 m.y.
Triassic	245 m.y.

Monzonite   See *igneous rocks.*

Moraine   Rock material deposited by a glacier. Usually unsorted debris from mud to boulder size.
Terminal Moraine   Deposited at the end of a glacier.
Lateral Moraine   Deposited along the sides of a glacier.

Mudflow   Explosive volcanoes blow ash and rocks (volcanic bombs) into the air. These pyroclastic rocks settle on the high slopes. During the next heavy rain the ash turns to mud and the accumulated rock debris and mud will flow down the slope and into the surrounding lowland. The flow is called a lahar and the resulting deposit a laharic breccia. A mudflow can be catastrophic. In 1985 a mudflow in Columbia killed 22,000 people.

Neogene   Please see *Tertiary*.

Normal fault   Vertical or near-vertical fault where the down-thrown side slips in the direction of dip of the fault.

Nuee Ardente   "Hot cloud", this is a very hot cloud of ash flowing laterally from an explosive volcano. The cloud is hot enough to vaporize any living thing in its path. Part of the matrix cools as glass and welds the ash into a hard rock. The rock deposited by a nuee ardente is an *ignimbrite* or *welded tuff*. Please see *Pyroclastic flow*.

Outwash   A sediment deposited by a meltwater stream emanating from a glacier.

Paleozoic   Geologic era from 570 to 245 m.y. geologic periods within this era

Period	Begins (m.y.)
Permian	290
Pennsylvanian	323
Mississippian	363
Devonian	409
Silurian	439
Ordovician	510
Cambrian	570

Pegmatite   A vein of extremely course grained granite. May contain economic amounts of rare minerals.

Placer   A clastic sedimentary deposit containing a valuable mineral or native metal in unusually high concentration. The metals are usually segregated because of their greater density.

Porphyry   An igneous rock containing megascopic mineral crystals (phenocrysts) suspended in a finely crystalline matrix.

Precambrian   Geologic time prior to 570 m.y.
     Proterozoic   Geologic time 2500 to 570 m.y.
     Archeozoic   Geologic time 4600 to 2500 m.y.

Provenance   Place of origin. Refers to the source of rock particles found in sediments.

Pyroclast   Fragment of volcanic material ejected during an eruption.

Pyroclastic flow A glowing cloud of volcanic ash, fragments of volcanic rock, ash and gases that pours down the slope of a volcano during an eruption at 60 to 100 miles per hour. It will incinerate every living thing in its path.

Quaternary Geologic period from 1.8 m.y. to Present. Epochs within this period:

Epochs	Begins
Holocene	13,000 years ago
Pleistocene	1.8 m.y. ago

Reverse fault Steeply dipping (>45 degrees) fault where the upthrown side is pushed up over the downthrown side.

Rift, Rift valley A fault bounded trough formed by tension (stetching) of the earth's crust. The Upper Arkansas rift valley is an example.

Rhubarb My favorite is rhubarb custard pie. (See US Highway 285 Road Log).

Rock Glacier Mass of rock fragments moving downhill as a gravity flow. Has the general appearance of an ice glacier. A series of transverse, arcuate ridges formed by the movement are recognizable on the upper surface of a rock glacier.

Rockslide The mass movement of large blocks of detached bedrock sliding more or less as a unit.

Sill (volcanic) Igneous rocks intruded sheet-like, parallel to the bedding of the intruded rocks.

Stock (volcanic) An intrusion with the characteristics of a batholith, but less that 100 km2 in area.

Strata Layers of sedimentary rock.

Stratigraphy The science of description, correlation, and classification of sedimentary rocks. Includes the interpretation of sedimentary environments of those strata.

Strike The geographic direction of a line formed by the intersection of a horizontal plane and the plane of tilted or vertical features, such as the bedding of sediment, igneous dikes, fault planes, etc

Syncline A fold in rocks in which the strata dip inward from both sides; a down fold. The opposite of *anticline*.

Tectonics. Pertaining to or designating the rock structure resulting from deformation of the earth's crust.

Terminal Moraine A deposit of glacial *till* deposited as an arcuate ridge across a valley that marks the farthest advance or maximum extent of a glacier.

Tertiary.   Geologic period from 65 to 1.8 million years ago. Epochs within this period:

Epoch	Begins (m.y. ago)	
Pliocene	5	] Neogene
Miocene	23	] "
Oligocene	40	
Eocene	57	
Paleocene	65	

Thrust fault   Shallow angle reverse fault (>45 degrees) **Overthrust fault**: Very shallow angle fault where the upthrown side travels some distance laterally over the down thrown side.

Thrust sheet   Rocks above an overthrust fault.

Till   An unstratified and poorly sorted sediment containing all sizes of fragments from clay to boulders, deposited by glacial action.

Tuff   Consolidated volcanic ash.

Volcanic neck The solidified material filling the vent of a dead volcano.

U-shaped Valley. Mountain valley having a cross sectional form of the letter U. Valley was eroded by a glacier. In contrast, mountain valleys eroded by streams have a V-shape.

Unconformity Break or gap in the geologic record. Usually a period of non-deposition and erosion. May apply to missing section in a sedimentary sequence. May also be applied to a large break in the record where igneous or metamorphic rocks are overlain by much younger sedimentary rocks.

Uplift   Refers to the epierogenic or local raising of the earth's crust by tectonic forces.

Welded tuff Deposits of volcanic ash that flowed in a cloud away from a volcano. When very hot at time of flow (nuee ardente), some of the ash particles will fuse as glass and thus weld the ash to a hard resistant rock (ignimbrite).

Xenoliths   Masses of country (surrounding) rock included in an intrusive rock mass.

Looking northwest from US 285 at Jefferson Hill, a Laramide Stock.